CALL YOURSELF
A HAMMERS FAN?

THE ULTIMATE
WEST HAM UNITED
QUIZ BOOK

DEDICATION

Continuing the tradition of the letter 'B' being involved with West Ham, this book is for my friend Carl Benson, Billy Bonds and in memory of the Boleyn.

ACKNOWLEDGEMENTS

My thanks are due again to Stuart Tibber and Michelle Grainger for their able assistance with this project.

RACING POST

CALL YOURSELF A HAMMERS FAN?

THE ULTIMATE
WEST HAM UNITED
QUIZ BOOK

MART MATTHEWS

First published by Pitch Publishing on behalf of Racing Post, 2022

Pitch Publishing
Pitch Publishing,
9 Donnington Park,
85 Birdham Road,
Chichester,
West Sussex, PO20 7AJ

www.pitchpublishing.co.uk
info@pitchpublishing.co.uk
www.racingpost.com/shop

A CIP catalogue record is available for this book
from the British Library.

ISBN 9781839501029

Typesetting and origination by Pitch Publishing

Printed and bound in Great Britain by TJ Books Ltd, Padstow

CONTENTS

INTRODUCTION — 8

1 ANYTHING GOES — 9
2 BIRTHPLACES — 10
3 THE BOLEYN - PART 1 — 11
4 THE BOLEYN - PART 2 — 13
5 BUBBLE BLOWING (FANS) — 15
6 CRYPTIC HAMMERS - PART 1 — 16
7 CRYPTIC HAMMERS - PART 2 — 17
8 CRYPTIC HAMMERS - PART 3 — 18
9 CRYPTIC HAMMERS - PART 4 — 19
10 CRYPTIC HAMMERS - PART 5 — 20
11 FA CUP FINAL OPPONENTS — 21
12 FOREIGN AFFAIRS - PART 1 — 22
13 FOREIGN AFFAIRS - PART 2 — 23
14 GOALKEEPERS — 24
15 GREENER GRASS (BEFORE) — 25
16 GREENER GRASS (AFTER) — 26
17 GREEN STREET GREATS - No. 1 - BILLY BONDS — 27
18 GREEN STREET GREATS - No. 2 - TREVOR BROOKING — 29
19 GREEN STREET GREATS - No. 3 - JOHNNY BYRNE — 31
20 GREEN STREET GREATS - No. 4 - GEOFF HURST — 33
21 GREEN STREET GREATS - No. 5 - FRANK LAMPARD SNR — 35
22 GREEN STREET GREATS - No. 6 - ALVIN MARTIN — 37
23 GREEN STREET GREATS - No. 7 - BOBBY MOORE — 38
24 GREEN STREET GREATS - No. 8 - MARK NOBLE — 40
25 GREEN STREET GREATS - No. 9 - PHIL PARKES — 42
26 GREEN STREET GREATS - No. 10 - VIC WATSON — 44
27 HAMMERS HEARD FROM (QUOTES) — 46
28 HELPING HANDS — 48
29 IF THE CAP FITS - PART 1 - ENGLAND — 50
30 IF THE CAP FITS - PART 2 - SCOTLAND AND WALES — 51
31 IF THE CAP FITS - PART 3 - NORTHERN IRELAND
   AND THE REPUBLIC OF IRELAND — 52
32 IF THE CAP FITS - PART 4 - OVERSEAS PLAYERS — 54
33 LATER IN LIFE — 55
34 MANAGERS — 56
35 MULTIPLE CHOICE — 57

36	POT LUCK	59
37	SEEING RED	61
38	TEN TOP HAMMERS - PART 1	63
39	TEN TOP HAMMERS - PART 2	65
40	THAMES IRONWORKS AND WEST HAM UNITED LEAGUE FOOTBALL - 1896-1915	67
41	TRANSFERS - 1945-1960 - PART 1	69
42	TRANSFERS - 1945-1960 - PART 2	70
43	TRANSFERS - 1960-1975 - PART 1	71
44	TRANSFERS - 1960-1975 - PART 2	72
45	TRANSFERS - 1975-1990 - PART 1	73
46	TRANSFERS - 1975-1990 - PART 2	74
47	TRANSFERS - 1990-2005 - PART 1	75
48	TRANSFERS - 1990-2005 - PART 2	76
49	TRANSFERS - 2005-2020 - PART 1	77
50	TRANSFERS - 2005-2020 - PART 2	78
51	TRUE OR FALSE	79
52	VENUES	80
53	WEST HAM UNITED IN THE EUROPEAN CUP WINNERS' CUP - PART 1 - 1964/65 AND 1965/66	81
54	WEST HAM UNITED IN THE EUROPEAN CUP WINNERS' CUP - PART 2 - 1975/76 AND 1980/81	83
55	WEST HAM IN EUROPE - 1999-2017 - PART 1	85
56	WEST HAM IN EUROPE - 1999-2017 - PART 2	86
57	WEST HAM UNITED IN FA CUP FINALS - PART 1 - CLUBS	88
58	WEST HAM UNITED IN FA CUP FINALS - PART 2 - PLAYERS	89
59	WEST HAM UNITED IN THE FA CUP - 1895-1915	90
60	WEST HAM UNITED IN THE FA CUP - 1919-39	92
61	WEST HAM UNITED IN THE FA CUP - 1945-60	94
62	WEST HAM UNITED IN THE FA CUP - THE 1960s	96
63	WEST HAM UNITED IN THE FA CUP - THE 1970s	97
64	WEST HAM UNITED IN THE FA CUP - THE 1980s	99
65	WEST HAM UNITED IN THE FA CUP - THE 1990s	101
66	WEST HAM UNITED IN THE LEAGUE - 1919-39	103
67	WEST HAM UNITED IN THE LEAGUE - 1946-60	105
68	WEST HAM UNITED IN THE LEAGUE - THE 1960s	107
69	WEST HAM UNITED IN THE LEAGUE - THE 1970s	109
70	WEST HAM UNITED IN THE LEAGUE - THE 1980s	111
71	WEST HAM UNITED IN THE LEAGUE - THE 1990s	113
72	WEST HAM UNITED IN LEAGUE CUP FINALS AND SEMI-FINALS - PART 1 - CLUBS	115

73 WEST HAM UNITED IN LEAGUE CUP FINALS
   AND SEMI-FINALS - PART 2 - PLAYERS   116
74 WEST HAM UNITED IN THE LEAGUE CUP - THE 1960s   117
75 WEST HAM UNITED IN THE LEAGUE CUP - THE 1970s   118
76 WEST HAM UNITED IN THE LEAGUE CUP - THE 1980s   120
77 WEST HAM UNITED IN THE LEAGUE CUP - THE 1990s   122
78 WEST HAM UNITED IN OTHER COMPETITIONS   124
79 WEST HAM UNITED - SEASON 2000/01   126
80 WEST HAM UNITED - SEASON 2001/02   128
81 WEST HAM UNITED - SEASON 2002/03   130
82 WEST HAM UNITED - SEASON 2003/04   132
83 WEST HAM UNITED - SEASON 2004/05   133
84 WEST HAM UNITED - SEASON 2005/06   134
85 WEST HAM UNITED - SEASON 2006/07   136
86 WEST HAM UNITED - SEASON 2007/08   138
87 WEST HAM UNITED - SEASON 2008/09   139
88 WEST HAM UNITED - SEASON 2009/10   140
89 WEST HAM UNITED - SEASON 2010/11   142
90 WEST HAM UNITED - SEASON 2011/12   144
91 WEST HAM UNITED - SEASON 2012/13   146
92 WEST HAM UNITED - SEASON 2013/14   148
93 WEST HAM UNITED - SEASON 2014/15   150
94 WEST HAM UNITED - SEASON 2015/16   151
95 WEST HAM UNITED - SEASON 2016/17   153
96 WEST HAM UNITED - SEASON 2017/18   155
97 WEST HAM UNITED - SEASON 2018/19   157
98 WEST HAM UNITED - SEASON 2019/20   159
99 WEST HAM UNITED - SEASON 2020/21   161
100 WILD CARD   163

ANSWERS   164

INTRODUCTION

Hello West Ham fans everywhere, and welcome to what I hope is the most comprehensive quiz on your club available. A word or two on the League Cup is required here. Since its inception in the 1960/61 season, it has had several sponsors, but to me it has always been the League Cup, and that it what it will be called in this quiz. My choice of ten players in the 'Green Street Greats' section will probably differ here and there from yours, but if it provokes a few disagreements it's all to the good.

QUIZ No. 1

ANYTHING GOES

1. Which three West Ham United players appeared in both the 1975 and 1980 FA Cup finals?

2. Which West Ham goalkeeper shares his surname with a famous hotel in Oxford that featured in the *Inspector Morse* TV series?

3. Which two players with West Ham connections appeared in 43 games between them for Blackburn Rovers when they won the Premier League in 1994/95?

4. World Cup heroes Moore, Hurst and Peters paraded the trophy at Upton Park in the first game of the new season on 20 August 1966. Who were their visitors?

5. What links the inter-war seasons of 1922/23, 1929/30, 1932/33, 1937/38 and 1938/39 concerning West Ham and the FA Cup competition?

6. Which player appeared just once as a substitute for West Ham in the league early in his career before winning the league and FA Cup with Liverpool in the late 80s and early 90s?

7. Which 21st-century Hammer ended up winning the league title with two different clubs?

8. What was highly unusual about Alvin Martin's hat-trick in an 8-1 win over Newcastle United at Upton Park on 21 April 1986?

9. Who are the only two players to score in more than one FA Cup final before joining the Hammers?

10. West Ham United played their first football league game on 30 August 1919, drawing 1-1 at Upton Park with Lincoln City. Their scorer that day shares a surname with a West Ham manager. What is that surname?

QUIZ No. 2

BIRTHPLACES

Here are ten West Ham United players. Use the clues in each case to locate their birthplace.

1. David James – the place where Shredded Wheat is manufactured?

2. Geoff Pike – famous blues guitarist

3. Ray Stewart – Scottish city with a jumps track

4. Bobby Moore – unpleasant sound emitted by dogs

5. Hayden Mullins – looking at a book

6. George Parris – sounds like a sick car

7. James Tompkins – add an Everly brother to the owner of Fawlty Towers

8. Luis Boa Morte – where Celtic won the European Cup

9. Billy Bonds – former building society

10. Andriy Yarmolenko – setting for Dostoyevsky's *Crime and Punishment*

QUIZ No. 3

THE BOLEYN - PART 1

1. Which ground did Thames Ironworks and West Ham United play on between 1895 and 1904?

2. Which club did they beat 3-0 on 1 September 1904 in their first game at their new Boleyn Ground?

3. What was the attendance at that first match?
   A) 5,000 B) 7,500 C) 10,000 D) 12,500

4. Unofficially, West Ham's biggest crowd at Upton Park is thought to be 43,528, and was set on 18 April 1936, but most sources now give that crowd as 41,500, and records were destroyed in the war, so no verification is possible. Which London club were the visitors that day, who ran out 3-1 winners?

5. Officially, the record was set on 17 October 1970 in a 2-2 draw watched by 43,322. The opposition that day were also the visitors in a friendly when floodlights were installed in 1953, and the first side to play West Ham when the ground was reopened in December 1944 after being hit in a V-1 rocket attack in August of that year. Who were those opponents on the three occasions?

6. The timber-and-corrugated-iron-covered enclosure at the front of the East Stand was demolished in 1968, with some of the atmosphere being demolished along with it. What was it affectionately known as?

7. The Trevor Brooking Stand that was built at the north end of the ground in 1995 originally had another name. What was it?

8. Previously, the Bobby Moore Stand had risen above what had been the South Bank in 1993, and in 2001 the new West Stand was built, becoming the largest single football stand in London. From 2001 to 2009 it was named after one of the club's sponsors, with an unintended nod towards the hooliganism of the 1970s and 1980s! What was it called?

9. Who officially opened the West Stand in 2001?

10. Who became the only West Ham player to score a goal in an international at Upton Park when he got the only goal of the match between England and Bulgaria under-21s on 9 October 1998?

QUIZ No. 4

THE BOLEYN - PART 2

1. Which club did West Ham share Upton Park with in the early 1990s?

2. Which two countries beginning with the same letter played a friendly at Upton Park on 10 August 2010?

3. What was the ground's postcode?

4. On 12 November 2014 Argentina beat Croatia 2-1 at Upton Park in an international friendly. Which ex-Hammer played for the Argentinians and who scored for them from the penalty spot?

5. Who were the only club to concede ten goals on the ground?

6. West Ham's biggest league win is 8-0, with both games in which this score occurred coming at Upton Park, the first in 1919 and the second in 1958. Which two teams left the ground in a depressed state?

7. England's only full international at Upton Park came against Australia on 12 February 2003. It cost £35 to get in and Sven-Goran Eriksson was clearly unaware that there is no such thing as a friendly when England play Australia at anything! The overcharged crowd had to watch England lose 3-1 as the master tactician, whose arse as usual never left his seat, changed the entire team at half-time! The fans' feelings to the fore again! It was hard for anyone to avoid making their England debut in the circumstances, but which player who later joined West Ham played his first game for his country that night while with Charlton Athletic?

8. Who did West Ham beat on the night of the last game at Upton Park on 10 May 2016, and who were they supposed to be playing their last home game against when the fixtures were announced at the start of the season? At least one coach might have left the ground in better condition if they'd played their original opponents!

9. Which player scored the last goal in the ground, as if you didn't know?

10. Who, on 21 August 2016, were West Ham's first opponents at the athletics track they had sold the soul of the club to play at?

QUIZ No. 5

BUBBLE BLOWING (FANS)

1. Watching West Ham can be an edge-of-the-seat experience, and this Hollywood director and West Ham fan knew more about suspense than anyone alive. Who was he?

2. Which West Ham fan has not often had to tell the Hammers faithful to 'turn it up'?

3. Which actor who played a West Ham fan so memorably on television in the 1960s and 70s was really a Spurs fan?

4. Holing the putt that won the Ryder Cup in 2002 was probably nearly as exciting as watching West Ham for which golfing Hammer?

5. Which West Ham fan struck gold in the 400m hurdles at the 1992 Olympic Games?

6. The author of the bestselling novel *Birdsong* is a West Ham fan. Who is he?

7. Who is the main presenter of West Ham TV?

8. Which singer, actor and Hammers fan has an appropriate county for a surname?

9. One of only 25 players in cricket history to score over 100 hundreds, this Essex opener and England Test cricketer is also a West Ham fan. Who is he?

10. When his rocker character clashed with Phil Daniels's mod in *Quadrophenia*, it was a case of West Ham vs Chelsea for the two actors. Who came out of the claret-and-blue corner for the Irons?

QUIZ No. 6

CRYPTIC HAMMERS - PART 1

You are given the dates of their time at West Ham, their total league appearances for the club, their position and a cryptic clue. Can you identify the player in each case?

1. Dock Green copper – centre-forward – 1952–54 – 39 games

2. *Catch 22* character – defender – 1981–87 – 146 games

3. Two kings and a famous footballer – defender – 1962–69 – 118 games

4. Flour producer – centre-forward – 1972–73 – 24 games

5. Boy next door – winger – 1979–82 – 73 games

6. Aussie word for food – winger – 1947–56 – 83 games

7. Country – winger – 1968–80 – 245 games

8. Cockney rhyming slang for 'neck' – goalkeeper – 1946–59 – 382 games

9. Scottish river comes out on top! – forward – 1969–75 – 186 games

10. Stiff breeze – defender – 1984–94 – 300 games

QUIZ No. 7

CRYPTIC HAMMERS – PART 2

You are given the dates of their time at West Ham, their total league appearances for the club, their position and a cryptic clue. Can you identify the player in each case?

1. Religious newspaper – defensive midfielder – 2000–07 – 158 games

2. Two Beatles for the price of one! – full-back – 2006–08 and 2012–14 – 95 games

3. Stick one letter on the front of his name and he'll build you a wall! – goalkeeper – 2013–18 – 125 games

4. Nineteenth-century novelist of some repute – midfielder – 1982–88 – 192 games

5. Masters golf champion 1991 – inside-forward – 1958–62 – 138 games

6. Fish or weapon – midfielder – 1975–86 – 291 games

7. Letters often start this way – forward – 1962–68 and 1970–69 games

8. Little – wing-half – 1936–47 – 108 games

9. Gloucestershire town – outside-right – 1951–56 – 13 games

10. Astronaut in 'The Eagle' – centre-forward – 1954–58 – 111 games

QUIZ No. 8

CRYPTIC HAMMERS - PART 3

You are given the dates of their time at West Ham, their total league appearances for the club, their position and a cryptic clue. Can you identify the player in each case?

1. West Ham World Cup hero becomes the victim of a scam – forward – 1982–84 – 61 games

2. US Open golf champion 2010 – right-back – 1970–78 – 249 games

3. *Robinson Crusoe* author – forward – 1999–2004 – 93 games

4. Well-known London street – attacking midfielder – 2013-15 – 69 games

5. County – attacking midfielder – 1976–89 – 358 games

6. Twenty-four hours – goalkeeper – 1973–78 – 194 games

7. Shares his surname with a famous goalkeeper who spent nearly all his career in the capital – forward – 1974–78 – 99 games

8. The next railway station to Twickenham – midfielder – 1983–84 – 39 games

9. Former golfer now on TV – centre-half – 1952–66 – 386 games

10. Liked nothing better than to get his head on one! – centre-forward – 1977–81 – 179 games

QUIZ No. 9

CRYPTIC HAMMERS - PART 4

You are given the dates of their time at West Ham, their total league appearances for the club, their position and a cryptic clue. Can you identify the player in each case?

1. Not a happy manager at Upton Park on 14 May 1995 – goalkeeper – 1967–79 – 240 games

2. Scottish king – wing-half – 1953–61 – 283 games

3. Richard – forward – 1953-62 – 326 games

4. More than one Richard – full-back – 1988-93 and 1994–99 – 262 games

5. Sounds like a European capital – defender – 1982–93 – 239 games

6. He takes it shaken but not stirred! – full-back – 1951-64 – 381 games

7. Add a letter – wing-half – 1967–87 – 663 games

8. Sounds like a Liverpool goalkeeper – half-back – 1950–57 – 238 games

9. Responsible for upkeep of church and churchyard – inside-forward – 1952-55 – 74 games

10. A figure somewhat higher in church circles – midfielder – 1989–91 – 98 games

QUIZ No. 10

CRYPTIC HAMMERS - PART 5

You are given the dates of their time at West Ham, their total league appearances for the club, their position and a cryptic clue. Can you identify the player in each case?

1. Excellent with a curry – defender – still at club

2. Colour and political party – goalkeeper – 2006–12 – 219 games

3. Archduke in Brazil – defender – 1996–2000 – 127 games

4. The first part is light, the second less so – outside-right – 1906–08 – 24 games

5. Shares a surname with a great trainer of horses – defensive midfielder – 2003–09 – 180 games

6. You could keep a lot of lions in one of these! – wing-half – 1901–04 – 91 games

7. Two kings, one from the Bible and one from a version of it – goalkeeper – 2001–04 – 91 games

8. Add one letter near the end of his surname and you produce two cars or people bumping into each other – midfielder – 2008–14 – 105 games

9. Michael Corleone's wife's name – centre-half – 1919–26 – 237 games

10. Occupation and *Eastenders* family – inside-forward – 1910–21 – 96 games

QUIZ No. 11

FA CUP FINAL OPPONENTS

1. Which football club played for Arsenal against West Ham in the 1980 FA Cup final?

2. Which Preston North End player became the youngest to play in an FA Cup final when they met West Ham in 1964?

3. Who is the only goalkeeper to keep a clean sheet against West Ham United in an FA Cup final?

4. Who is the only player to score twice in an FA Cup final against West Ham?

5. Which member of the Arsenal side that played West Ham in the 1980 FA Cup final later played for them?

6. Five goalkeepers have faced West Ham in an FA Cup final with just two of them being born outside the British Isles. Who are they?

7. Who is the only player to score a goal in an FA Cup final for West Ham by putting through his own net?

8. The surname of one of the members of West Ham's 1975 FA Cup final side is the same as a member of the Bolton Wanderers team that played them in 1923, and of a member of the Arsenal team that met them in 1980. What is that surname?

9. Which player on the Preston North End side that played West Ham in the 1964 final had turned out previously for Bolton Wanderers in the 1958 final against Manchester United?

10. The Fulham side that lost to West Ham in the 1975 FA Cup final contained one player who doubles as a town in North Wales and another who doubles as a town in south-east England. Who are the two players?

FOREIGN AFFAIRS - PART 1

In common with many other clubs towards the end of the last century, and increasingly in this one, West Ham have recruited from abroad, with various degrees of success. From which club did each of the ten players below come from?

1. Carlos Tevez

2. Issa Diop

3. Pablo Fornals

4. Winston Reid

5. Manuel Lanzini

6. Frederic Kanoute

7. Arthur Masuaku

8. Tomas Soucek

9. Cheikhou Kouyate

10. Ludek Miklosko

FOREIGN AFFAIRS - PART 2

In common with many other clubs towards the end of the last century, and increasingly in this one, West Ham have recruited from abroad, with various degrees of success. From which club did each of the ten players below come from?

1. Tomas Repka

2. Felipe Anderson

3. Sebastien Haller

4. Adrian

5. Dimitri Payet

6. Marc Vivien-Foe

7. Andriy Yarmolenko

8. Angelo Ogbonna

9. Scott Minto

10. Sofiane Feghouli

QUIZ No. 14

GOALKEEPERS

1. West Ham United have fielded a different goalkeeper in each of their five FA Cup finals. Which two of them have a surname beginning with the same letter?

2. Phil Parkes has a decent claim to the title of West Ham United's greatest goalkeeper. His career was dominated by two clubs, the other being Queens Park Rangers. For which of the two did he play the most league games?

3. Who is the only West Ham goalkeeper to have played in an FA Cup final for three clubs?

4. Which West Ham goalkeeper topped the bowling averages in the 1960s while playing cricket for Worcestershire?

5. West Ham goalkeeper Ludek Miklosko was popular with fans, but why did he get a standing ovation when he took the field at Ewood Park with West Ham on 2 December 1995?

6. Which other London club did West Ham goalkeeper Mervyn Day play for?

7. After 240 league games for West Ham, Bobby Ferguson kept goal just five times for which Yorkshire club?

8. Which West Ham goalkeeper played for Manchester United in the 2005 FA Cup final?

9. Which Scottish goalkeeper played 85 league games for West Ham between 1981 and 1988?

10. Noel Dwyer, Brian Rhodes, Lawrie Leslie and Peter Grotier all played in goal for West Ham from the late 1950s to the early 1970s. Who made the most league starts?

QUIZ No. 15

GREENER GRASS (BEFORE)

All these players appeared in an FA Cup final for another club before joining West Ham. Can you identify them in each case?

1. Who came to West Ham after being sent off for Manchester City in the 2013 final?

2. Who came to West Ham after playing for Manchester United in the 1999 final?

3. Who came to West Ham after playing for Arsenal in the 1971 and 1972 finals?

4. Which three members of the Liverpool side in the 2012 final eventually ended up at West Ham?

5. Who came to West Ham after playing for Spurs in the 1962 and 1967 finals?

6. Who came to West Ham after playing for Manchester United in the 1977 final

7. Who came to West Ham after appearing for Liverpool in the 1992 final?

8. Who hit the ground running at West Ham after appearing for Manchester United in the 2016 and 2018 finals?

9. Which two Arsenal men ended up at West Ham after playing in the 2014 final?

10. Which player eventually joined West Ham after playing in the 1978, 1979 and 1980 finals for Arsenal, the last one against the Hammers?

GREENER GRASS (AFTER)

All these players appeared in an FA Cup final for another club after leaving West Ham. Can you identify them in each case?

1. After leaving West Ham he figured in the 2008 cup final for Portsmouth and the 2012 final with Liverpool.

2. After leaving West Ham he played for Stoke City in the 2011 cup final.

3. After leaving West Ham he played in two finals for Chelsea in 2007 and 2010.

4. After leaving West Ham he played in the emotional final with Everton against Liverpool in 1989.

5. After leaving West Ham he captained Manchester United to their 1963 cup final success, but if he had stayed another year or two with West Ham he would have won it with them instead.

6. After leaving West Ham he won and lost a cup final with Manchester City in 2011 and 2013.

7. After leaving West Ham he played against them in the 1975 final for Fulham.

8. After leaving West Ham he played for Portsmouth in the 2010 final.

9. After leaving West Ham he played in four finals in the 1990s for Manchester United.

10. After leaving West Ham he played in five finals for Chelsea this century.

QUIZ No. 17

GREEN STREET GREATS –
No. 1 – BILLY BONDS

1. The £50,000 that West Ham United paid Charlton Athletic for Billy Bonds was probably the greatest investment the club ever made. Had he played more or fewer than 100 league games for Charlton?

2. West Ham managed to lose his first and last games for the club with nearly 21 years between them, going down 3-2 at home in 1967 on his debut and 2-1 away on his swansong. Both matches were against teams beginning with 'S'. Who were they?

3. Billy's first league goal and first FA Cup goal for West Ham were both against London clubs, the former coming in a 2-1 home win on 23 December 1967 and the latter in the FA Cup fourth round, also at home, in a 1-1 draw on 28 January 1978. Which two clubs from the capital did they play?

4. Billy Bonds scored more League Cup goals for West Ham than the combined total of his goals in the FA Cup and European competition. True or false?

5. Which club did he score home and away against in the league in 1973/74?

6. In the days when outfield players wore 2 to 11 on their backs and you didn't have to study an infantilised, oversized and overpriced programme for ten minutes to work out who the number 37 was, Billy Bonds played for West Ham with eight different numbers on his back, excluding the no. 12 he also wore as substitute. Which were the only two outfield numbers he didn't wear?

7. How are Cardiff City, Coventry City, Darlington, Stoke City and Tranmere Rovers linked in relation to Billy's West Ham career?

8. Billy scored league goals against four clubs beginning with 'C'. Chelsea, Coventry City and Crystal Palace constituted three of them. Who was the fourth?

9. Chelsea figure in Billy's West Ham career because he did two things against them that he didn't do against any other club. The first came at Stamford Bridge on 9 September 1972 in a 3-1 win and the second at Upton Park on 2 March 1974 when the Hammers won 3-0. The second one's not too hard, but for the first one I urge you to concentrate on the word 'Chelsea'. Which two unique events in his West Ham career did Billy Bonds achieve against the west-London club?

10. Billy Bonds scored goals at Upton Park in Europe against Den Haag of Holland in 1976 and Poli Timisoara of Romania in 1980, but he scored just once away from home in Europe and it came in a 2-2 draw in the European Cup Winners' Cup on 17 September 1975 against Lahden Reipas. Which country did they represent?

QUIZ No. 18

GREEN STREET GREATS – No. 2 – TREVOR BROOKING

1. Trevor Brooking was a silky-smooth midfielder for West Ham who made his league debut for the Hammers in a 3-3 away draw on 29 August 1967 against a team that share West Ham's colours. Who were they?

2. He scored his first goal in the league for West Ham in a 4-2 Boxing Day win in 1967 at Upton Park and followed that up by scoring away against the same opposition four days later when West Ham repeated the 4-2 scoreline. Therefore, he had scored in two games against one club before he scored against anyone else. Who were that Midlands club?

3. Which other Midlands club were the only side he scored against in the FA Cup at Upton Park during his career? The goal came in a 2-1 replay win in the third round on 8 January 1980.

4. His most famous goal in a West Ham shirt also came in that competition when he used his head in more ways than one to divert a cross shot into the net in the 1980 FA Cup final against Arsenal. Whose intended shot did he redirect to win the cup for West Ham?

5. Trevor Brooking scored league goals for West Ham against both clubs from six cities. Those cities were Manchester, Liverpool, Birmingham, Sheffield, Nottingham and Bristol. True or false?

6. Trevor won 47 England caps, but scored twice in an international for England just once. It came in a 3-1 away win on 6 June 1981 in a World Cup qualifier with a lot riding on it. Who did England beat that day?

7. It was the same story for West Ham in Europe. Trevor scored twice on just one occasion and like the England game it was a vital match, the European Cup Winners' Cup semi-final second leg of 1975/76 and his goals put West Ham through to the final. Which German club did they eliminate from the competition?

8. Bolton Wanderers, Bristol City, Barnsley and Bury are linked to each other by being the only clubs beginning with 'B' that Trevor Brooking did what against?

9. Which London club did Trevor score against home and away in the 1976/77 season when West Ham won 5-3 at home and lost 2-1 away?

10. Trevor Brooking's only West Ham hat-trick came in his first season with the club on 6 April in a 5-0 league win at Upton Park over which club?

QUIZ No. 19

GREEN STREET GREATS –
No. 3 – JOHNNY BYRNE

1. You get beautiful creative players who don't get enough goals and goalscorers who aren't great to watch outside that, but 'Budgie' Byrne, as he was widely known, had both these qualities. That led him to be called 'the English Di Stefano'. High praise indeed. West Ham paid Crystal Palace £65,000 for his signature, and although he topped West Ham's league goalscorers chart on two occasions, his biggest haul came in Palace's promotion season in 1960/61. How many of their 110 goals did he score?

2. What was unique about his selection for England under-23s while at the Selhurst Park club?

3. His first and last league games for West Ham were against clubs beginning with 'S'. His debut came in a 0-0 away draw on 17 March 1962, and his last game, in which he scored in a 2-2 draw at Upton Park, came on 11 February 1967. Who were West Ham's two opponents?

4. His first FA Cup goal for the Irons came in a 2-1 away win in a third-round replay on 20 February 1963 against a London club that he went on to play for. Who were they?

5. It would have endeared him to West Ham fans that he scored more league goals against this team than any other. Who were they?

6. Johnny Byrne's England record of eight goals in 11 games is excellent, and he scored twice against both Switzerland and Uruguay. However, he went one better than that on 17 May 1964 when his hat-trick included an 87th-minute winner in England's 4-3 away win against which country?

7. Johnny Byrne scored League Cup hat-tricks in successive seasons at Upton Park in 1962 and 1963, both coming in 6-0 wins. The first came against a side from the South West and the second against a side from the North West who are no longer in the league. Who are the two clubs?

8. Who are the only two clubs that Johnny Byrne has scored against in both domestic cup competitions, one from London and the other from a few miles down the M4?

9. Johnny Byrne's first West Ham goal came in the league on 20 April 1962 in a 4-1 win at Upton Park against which club who are one of the eight he has scored against in the League Cup?

10. Which country did Johnny Byrne go to to finish his career as a player and then go on to management in that same country?

QUIZ No. 20

GREEN STREET GREATS -
No. 4 - GEOFF HURST

1. After 25 games at right-half, Ron Greenwood switched Geoff Hurst into the attack and his career took off. The same club that he put the No. 10 shirt on against for the first time at Upton Park on 3 September 1962 were also the club he played his last league game against on that same ground on 15 April 1972. Who were they?

2. Which two other clubs did he play for after leaving West Ham?

3. Which two London clubs did he score against on the road to Wembley in 1964, his goal in the third round being his first FA Cup goal for the club?

4. In that same season West Ham knocked out one club from both domestic cup competitions and Geoff scored against them in all three games they played. Who were they?

5. Geoff made his England debut against West Germany in February 1966 and then, five months later, scored a hat-trick against the same country in a match you might have seen! He scored one other hat-trick for his country, boosted by two penalties, on 12 March 1969 in a 5-0 win at Wembley against which nation?

6. The club he scored his first hat-trick against on 11 December 1965 in a 4-3 win at Upton Park are geographically close to the only side he scored six times against, with that also coming at Upton Park in an 8-0 win on 19 October 1968. Who are the two teams?

7. Geoff Hurst twice scored four times in a game, the first time on Bonfire Night of 1966 in a 6-1 home win over a London club. The second occasion was in a League Cup tie on the same ground on 11 October 1967 in a 4-1 win over Lancastrian opposition. The two clubs share their colours. Who were they?

8. There were two occasions in Geoff's England career when he scored the only goal of the game in a World Cup tournament, one coming in 1966 and the other in 1970. Which two countries were on the receiving end?

9. What did Geoff Hurst do against Swindon Town and Hereford United that he didn't do against any other clubs?

10. What is the link between the cities of Manchester and Athens in Geoff Hurst's career?

QUIZ No. 21

GREEN STREET GREATS - No. 5 - FRANK LAMPARD SNR

1. Frank Lampard made his West Ham debut on 18 November 1967 in a 3-2 home defeat, going on to play 19 league games that season. A broken leg kept him out of the following season until his reappearance in the season's last game when he played away in a 1-1 draw against the same club he had made his debut against. Who were they?

2. His first and last goal for West Ham in the League Cup came on 3 September 1969 in a 4-2 win at Upton Park against a well-known building society. Who were they?

3. He scored away from home for West Ham on two London grounds, one of those being White Hart Lane. However, the other one he scored on happened on two occasions, firstly when he scored his first league goal on 19 December 1970 and then again on Boxing Day 1973 in a 4-2 win. Which London ground was it?

4. Frank's magnificent appearances record for the Hammers stretched over 18 seasons, but in only one of those seasons did he play every league game for the club. Which one?

5. Frank Lampard scored just once in the European Cup Winners' Cup for West Ham. It came in a 3-1 second-leg win at Upton Park on 17 March 1976 against which Dutch club?

6. Frank deserved more than his two England caps that were spread out over an eight-year period. He played against a country that no longer exists, and a country where a match against them in a different sport is always rather competitive. Who were his two caps against?

7. Who were the only other club that Frank played for in his career?

8. He was responsible for two vital goals when West Ham won the FA Cup in 1975 and again in 1980. In 1975 his goal contributed to a 2-1 away win in the third round against which southern club?

9. Then, on 16 April 1980, he came up with the winner in extra time of the FA Cup semi-final replay at Elland Road against which club?

10. A tough one to end with. Who were the only club that Frank scored against at Upton Park in the 1970s and the 1980s? I'll reduce the odds significantly by telling you that West Ham have played in an FA Cup final against them. Easier?

QUIZ No. 22

GREEN STREET GREATS -
No. 6 - ALVIN MARTIN

1. Towering centre-half Alvin Martin came on as a substitute for his first game when they lost 4-1 in the Midlands on 18 March 1978. Who were they playing?

2. However, it was a different story the first time he started a game for the Irons because he scored in their 2-1 win in Yorkshire on 8 April 1978. Who did they beat?

3. Alvin played 17 times for England, the first of which came against which South American country on 12 May 1981 in a game England lost 1-0?

4. In a career spanning nearly 20 years, did he play more or fewer than 600 games in all competitions for the club?

5. Which Midlands club were the only one he scored against in three different league games at Upton Park?

6. Alvin Martin scored six goals in the League Cup for West Ham United. They came singly against Barnsley, Bury, Oldham Athletic and Sunderland, but which Midlands club did he score twice against?

7. Besides Upton Park, he found the net on just one other London ground when West Ham won there 3-2 on 2 October 1982. Which ground was it?

8. Who were the only club that Alvin Martin scored against both home and away in the league for West Ham?

9. How many goals did Alvin Martin score for West Ham in the FA Cup and European competition combined?

10. Which London club did Alvin play 17 times for when he left West Ham in 1996?

QUIZ No. 23

GREEN STREET GREATS –
No. 7 – BOBBY MOORE

1. In the 1958/59 season Bobby Moore made his West Ham debut, playing in five league games. They lost away at Nottingham Forest, Burnley and Leeds United, but won both the home games he played in by 3-2 and 5-1 against two teams from the same city. Which one?

2. There was one club from the Midlands that he usually looked forward to playing against. They were the first one that he scored against in the league, the only one that he scored against twice in a game, and the team he scored the most times against in his career. Who were they?

3. When Bobby Moore received his first England cap in 1962 they were beaten away by 4-1. When he got his 100th cap in 1973 they won away by 5-0. The two games took place against which two countries?

4. Which of the following six London clubs was the only one Bobby failed to score against in the league or either domestic cup competition – Arsenal, Charlton Athletic, Chelsea, Fulham, Queens Park Rangers and Tottenham Hotspur?

5. What was the only English club ground that he scored on while playing for England? His goal came in a 1-1 draw with Poland on 5 January 1966.

6. Bobby has the rare distinction of captaining a team to win a trophy three years running at Wembley, in 1964, 1965 and 1966; the first two with West Ham and the third with England. Six West Ham players scored in those three games, but only two share the same first letter of their surname. Who are they?

7. Who were the only club that Bobby Moore scored against in both the league and the League Cup?

8. Whose England appearances record did he break when he received the 106th of his eventual 108 caps for England?

9. Although his final outing in a West Ham shirt was for the reserves against Plymouth Argyle, who did West Ham play on the occasion of his last league game, which took place at Upton Park on New Year's Day of 1974, and who were the visitors to that ground for his final FA Cup tie four days later?

10. As is well known, Bobby ended his career across the capital with Fulham, playing against the Hammers in the 1975 FA Cup final. The ground on which he played his final game was the home of the club he had led West Ham out to play against in the 1959 FA Youth Cup final all those years ago. Which ground was it?

QUIZ No. 24

GREEN STREET GREATS –
No. 8 – MARK NOBLE

1. A club that Mark Noble played five games for on loan in 2006 share their colours with the club that he made his West Ham league debut against in January 2005. Who are the two clubs?

2. Another club that he was loaned out to in 2006 was Ipswich Town, and it was with that club that he scored his first goal in professional football on 12 September 2006 against which Midlands club?

3. He's the only modern player on my list of ten and his name is a good summing up of the feelings he has for the club, working tirelessly on its behalf. You could tell what it meant to him when after he had scored his first Premier League goal for the club at Upton Park on the night of 4 March 2007 they contrived to lose the game 4-3 at the death to which club?

4. When I consider some of the players who have been capped numerous times for England I find it difficult to see how he has been overlooked time and time again. He did, however, turn out a number of times for England under-21s and scored against two countries, one from Eastern Europe and the other from closer to home. Who were they?

5. Albeit that a significant number have come from the penalty spot, nevertheless Mark Noble has found the net over 50 times for the club in league football. Who is the only player on this list to currently have scored more league goals for West Ham – Ray Stewart, Trevor Morley, Frank McAvennie, Paul Goddard, Clyde Best and Billy Bonds?

6. On 10 April 2021 Mark Noble played his 400th Premier League game for West Ham in a 3-2 home win over which club?

7. Mark Noble's 205th Premier League game came against Newcastle United on 29 November 2014 and saw him overtake which West Ham player's Premier League appearances record?

8. Which club from the south coast did Mark score his first West Ham goal against in the third round of the FA Cup in January 2007 that helped West Ham to a 3-0 win?

9. Mark Noble made his 500th appearance for West Ham in a 3-1 win in the strange month of July 2020 after finishing the previous season with two goals in a 4-1 win over the same club on that season's last day. Which club?

10. At the start of the 2020/21 season, Mark Noble went public to voice his opinion that West Ham should not have let which player leave the club?

QUIZ No. 25

GREEN STREET GREATS −
No. 9 − PHIL PARKES

1. Phil Parkes was born in a place that shares its name with a Spurs player who won an FA Cup winners' medal with them in 1991. Where was Phil born?

2. Bert Williams, one of England's greatest goalkeepers, started out at the same Midlands club that Phil Parkes started his career at. Which club was it?

3. Phil was unfortunate to be around at the same time as those two great goalkeepers Peter Shilton and Ray Clemence, and won just one England cap when he kept a clean sheet in a 0-0 away draw on 3 April 1974 against which country?

4. Which other West Ham player made his international debut in that game, and which West Ham player was appearing for his country for the 66th time?

5. West Ham, a Second Division club at the time, broke the transfer record for a goalkeeper when they persuaded Phil to move across the capital from Queens Park Rangers in February 1979. Did they pay more or less than half a million for his services?

6. By a strange coincidence the team he made his Hammers debut against in a 3-0 home win on 24 February 1979 were the same team that he played his last game for the club against on Valentine's Day of 1990. Unlike the earlier and happier occasion this one really did turn into a St Valentine's Day massacre as West Ham lost 6-0. Which club beat them?

7. As well as being Phil's last game for the club, it also brought a managerial career to an end. Whose?

8. By keeping a clean sheet when West Ham won the FA Cup against Arsenal in 1980 he became the only West Ham goalkeeper to do so before or since in a Wembley final. True or false?

9. He joined another club in 1990 but played just three times for them before his retirement. Who were they?

10. A tough one to end with. In his time at Upton Park, Phil Parkes was an ever-present in the league in four seasons, and only four other goalkeepers played for the club during his time. Who were they?

QUIZ No. 26

GREEN STREET GREATS –
No. 10 – VIC WATSON

1. Vic Watson's exploits as West Ham's centre-forward in the inter-war years echo down the years. The only man to score more than 300 goals for the club did it when there was no League Cup and no European competitions. His greatest season was perhaps 1929/30 when he scored how many league goals for West Ham?

2. Two teams beginning with 'C' figure in Vic's early West Ham career. His first away game and first home game were against one of them while the other provided him with his first West Ham goal in a 1-0 away win on 4 October 1920, and his first hat-trick, also away in a 3-1 win on 30 December 1922. Who were the two teams?

3. On the way to Wembley in 1923 Vic scored three vital goals that kept West Ham in the competition. They came against two teams who play on the coast in the second and fourth rounds, one involving a replay, with all three matches ending 1-1. Who were the two clubs?

4. In the league in 1931/32 how many games in succession did Vic Watson score in?

5. Who were the only club that Vic scored three league hat-tricks against?

6. Which book of the Bible did Vic Watson score against in the FA Cup in 1928/29 and in 1932/33?

7. There was one Yorkshire team that Vic loved playing against. On 9 February 1929 he ran riot at Upton Park when he grabbed six goals in the home side's 8-2 win. Then, on 25 January 1930, he got all four when West Ham beat them 4-1 in the FA Cup, and then for good measure he got the three that they won a league game with by 3-0 on 22 March 1930. Who were sick of the sight of him?

8. Vic got one FA Cup hat-trick against another London club. It came on 8 January 1927 at Upton Park in a 3-2 third-round win over which club?

9. Vic Watson scored four times in a 5-1 win at Crystal Palace on 31 March 1923. Which player who shared his first name also scored four times for West Ham, this time against Blackburn Rovers, some 35 years later?

10. Vic scored four in a game on one other occasion. It came in a 7-0 home win on the first day of September 1930. He also scored one FA Cup semi-final goal which came on 18 March 1933. The two clubs he scored against play in the same city. Which one?

QUIZ No. 27

HAMMERS HEARD FROM (QUOTES)

1. 'I lay in bed the other night thinking about strikers. It's a few years ago now but I can remember when there were always much better things to do in bed.' Like wondering what formation to play with at the weekend perhaps! Which West Ham manager is quoted here?

2. 'The man who comes to take care of my piranhas told me that if I left West Ham he would kill all my fish.' Which West Ham player was relieved he didn't end up at Manchester United?

3. 'When I first saw the pictures of what I did I was ashamed. The worst thing was when people phoned my missus, who's six months pregnant, and said, "What's it like living with a lunatic?"' Which West Ham player about what?

4. 'There should be a law against him. He knows what's happening 20 minutes before anyone else.' Which Scottish manager about which West Ham player?

5. 'All that "happy losers" stuff is a load of cobblers. I hate losing.' Which West Ham man rejects the 'purist' stereotype applied to the Hammers?

6. 'After Bobby Moore, I'm probably the greatest player to come out of West Ham, which is to their credit.' Which ex-Hammer comes over all humble?

7. 'Floats like a butterfly and stings like one too.' Which famous manager doesn't rate which player who is considered an Upton Park great?

8. 'He has terrible dress sense. I think he gets freebie clothes from some weird place in Wales.' Which West Ham manager on which West Ham player?

9.   'I always thought golf was a poof's game. Now I prefer it to football.' Which West Ham defender now prefers the smaller ball?

10. 'The first time he and I played together in the same side was for the Essex Schools cricket team.' Which West Ham legend on which other West Ham legend?

QUIZ No. 28

HELPING HANDS

All these players have scored own goals while playing against West Ham United. Can you identify them in each case?

1. Which Charlton Athletic defender put through his own net twice against West Ham, the first time when they lost 5-0 at Upton Park on Boxing Day 2000, and the second time when they beat West Ham 4-2 at The Valley on 22 January 2003, when West Ham's other goal was also generously donated by the opposition although it didn't make much difference?

2. Which Spurs player scored one of West Ham's goals when they won 2-0 at Upton Park on 3 May 2014?

3. Which Everton full-back put through his own net in a 1-1 draw with West Ham at Upton Park on 28 December 2010?

4. West Ham's consolation goal when they were beaten 4-1 at Anfield on 7 December 2013 came from a Liverpool defender. Which one?

5. An Aston Villa player who shares his surname with a well-known golfer scored West Ham's goal when they went down 2-1 at Villa Park on 10 February 2013. Who was he?

6. Three goalkeepers, one of which later joined the Irons, scored for West Ham through own goals. The first came in September 2005 when West Ham won 3-2 against Fulham at Craven Cottage, the second in March 2006 when they beat Bolton Wanderers 2-1 in an FA Cup fifth-round replay, and the third when West Ham beat Sunderland 3-1 at Upton Park in October 2007. Who were the three goalkeepers?

7. Which Hull City player, who shares his surname with a northern racecourse, scored for West Ham when they won 2-1 at Upton Park on 26 March 2014?

8. A Wolves player whose surname begins with the last letter of the alphabet put through his own net when West Ham won 2-0 at Upton Park on the first day of 2011. Who was he?

9. Which Newcastle United player who later joined the Hammers scored one of West Ham's goals when they lost 4-2 at home to the Geordies on 17 December 2005?

10. Which giant Blackburn Rovers centre-half wasn't dancing for joy when he contributed a goal to West Ham's 4-1 win over his side on 30 August 2008.

QUIZ No. 29

IF THE CAP FITS - PART 1 - ENGLAND

Currently 27 post-war players have appeared in an England international while at West Ham. Here are ten questions about them.

1. Three players gained their sole England cap while at West Ham. The first came in 1960, the second in 1982 and the last in 2008. Who were the three players?

2. Two surnames have appeared twice among West Ham players capped for England. What are those two surnames?

3. Bobby Moore is the only West Ham post-war player with a surname beginning with 'M' to be capped for England. True or false?

4. Which three players who earned England caps while at Upton Park were also capped while with Spurs?

5. Who is the only West Ham goalkeeper to be capped post-war for England while at the club?

6. One letter has appeared five times at the front of a surname of a West Ham player capped post-war by England. What is that letter?

7. Which two men who were capped for England while at West Ham were also capped while at Crystal Palace?

8. Trevor Brooking and Geoff Hurst are very close to each other when it comes to England caps gained. Who has the most and what is the gap between them?

9. Who is the only West Ham player to also be capped while at Manchester City?

10. Rio Ferdinand, Stuart Pearce and Martin Peters were all capped at West Ham and elsewhere. Can you put them in the right order concerning the total number of caps they won?

QUIZ No. 30

IF THE CAP FITS - PART 2
- SCOTLAND AND WALES

1. Which two central-defenders, both capped for Wales while at West Ham this century, gained their first caps for their country while at Cardiff City?

2. Which prolific West Ham goalscorer gained his only Scottish cap in 1959?

3. Craig Bellamy won 78 Welsh caps. How many other clubs besides West Ham was he capped with?

4. This player, with 67, holds the overall record number of caps for Scotland by a player capped while at West Ham. He also won caps at Derby County and Blackburn Rovers. Who was he?

5. John Hartson won 51 Welsh caps while with five clubs. West Ham were obviously one of them, and three others were Arsenal, Celtic and Coventry City. Which London club is missing from the list?

6. Which two players were the only ones to win caps for Scotland while at West Ham in the 1980s?

7. Which classy inside-forward was West Ham's first post-war Welsh international in the late 1950s?

8. This midfielder's 26 Scottish caps came between 1999 and 2004, and were achieved at Everton and Sunderland as well as West Ham. Who was he?

9. His 65 caps for Wales came between 1990 and 2005, the last of them while he was at Upton Park after spells at Swansea City, Oxford United, Sunderland and Fulham. Who was he?

10. Robert Snodgrass has been West Ham's most recent Scottish cap. Which other two clubs was he capped with prior to his time at West Ham?

QUIZ No. 31

IF THE CAP FITS - PART 3 - NORTHERN IRELAND AND THE REPUBLIC OF IRELAND

1. He got his first cap for Northern Ireland while at West Ham in 2002 and received another 38 along the way while at Cheltenham Town, Barnsley, Scunthorpe United and Peterborough United. Who was he?

2. Which West Ham player this century has had the Republic of Ireland caps he won at the club sandwiched between those he won at Motherwell and Middlesbrough?

3. Which West Ham player won 59 caps for Northern Ireland, earning them with, besides West Ham, Luton Town, Southampton, Crystal Palace and QPR?

4. Between 1996 and 2006 who won 63 caps for the Republic of Ireland while with Birmingham City, Coventry City, West Ham United and Sunderland?

5. Which centre-forward made 46 appearances for Northern Ireland between 1985 and 1996 while with Blackburn Rovers, Swindon Town, Leicester City, Bradford City, West Ham United, Bournemouth and Reading?

6. Full-back Chris Hughton was capped for the Republic of Ireland while at Spurs and West Ham. Did he win more or fewer than 50 caps?

7. His haul of caps for Northern Ireland was an impressive 71, and, besides West Ham, he won them at Manchester City, two other London clubs and Strasbourg between 1992 and 2005. Who was he?

8. He scored nine goals in 41 internationals for the Republic of Ireland between 1996 and 2006, representing his country while with two foreign clubs as well as the three Ws of Wigan Athletic, Wimbledon and West Ham United. Who was he?

9. Who are the only two West Ham United goalkeepers to be capped post-war by Northern Ireland while at Upton Park, the first in the late 1980s and the other this century?

10. Which player, capped for the Republic of Ireland while at Upton Park, had previously been capped at four Italian clubs?

IF THE CAP FITS - PART 4 - OVERSEAS PLAYERS

All the following West Ham United players were capped for their countries. Which country was it in each case?

1. Valon Behrami

2. Shaka Hislop

3. Lucas Neill

4. Sergei Rebrov

5. Marc Rieper

6. Leroy Rosenior

7. Nolberto Solano

8. Jonathan Spector

9. Francois Van der Elst

10. Paulo Wanchope

QUIZ No. 33

LATER IN LIFE

All these West Ham players achieved something after their playing days. Can you identify them from the descriptions in each case?

1. Which two West Ham players went on to manage Manchester United, the first from 1971/72 and the second from 1977/81?

2. Which West Ham player was England's caretaker manager in 2012?

3. Which West Ham goalkeeper became manager of Carlisle United in 1996?

4. Which West Ham player was Manchester City's manager when they met Spurs in the 1981 FA Cup final?

5. Which three post-war West Ham players have all managed Chelsea?

6. Which West Ham player won the FA Cup as a manager with Portsmouth in 2008?

7. Which West Ham player has had two spells of management at Manchester City?

8. Which West Ham player managed Blackburn Rovers in 2008?

9. Which West Ham player managed Sheffield United in 1981?

10. In this century which two West Ham players have managed Newcastle United?

QUIZ No. 34

MANAGERS

1. In a phenomenal two spells of longevity in the job which two West Ham managers accounted for almost half a century of running the club between 1902 and 1950?

2. Who is the only West Ham United manager to win the FWA Footballer of the Year award as a player?

3. Which West Ham United manager had a 100 per cent win record as a national team manager?

4. Only two West Ham United managers share the same first name. Who are they?

5. Who is the only man to take charge of West Ham in two different centuries?

6. Who is the only West Ham manager to win a European trophy with the club?

7. Three ex-players have helped West Ham out by taking the role of caretaker manager. One did it in 1990, another on two occasions in 2003, and the third twice between 2008 and 2011. Who are the three men?

8. Who are the only two men to manage West Ham whose surnames end with the letter 'I'?

9. Who is the only manager to guide West Ham to two FA Cup victories?

10. Who is the only West Ham United manager to lead out a team as manager in a Champions League final?

QUIZ No. 35

MULTIPLE CHOICE

1. What was the cost in 'new' money of a ticket to stand on the South Bank for West Ham United's first game in the European Cup Winners' Cup against La Gantoise on 23 September 1964?
   A) 20p B) 30p C) 40p D) 50p

2. Who were the only British club to win a European trophy before West Ham?
   A) Liverpool B) Manchester United C) Spurs D) Celtic

3. When West Ham sold Syd Puddefoot for a British record fee of £5,000 in February of 1922, to which Scottish club did he go?
   A) Falkirk B) St. Mirren C) Dundee D) Airdrie

4. Which one of these London clubs was the only one not to play top-flight post-war football before West Ham?
   A) Fulham B) Charlton Athletic C) Brentford D) QPR

5. Which club did West Ham play their first Premier League game against on 14 August 1993?
   A) Leeds United B) Coventry City C) Wimbledon
   D) Sheffield Wednesday

6. Who had the longest spell of management at West Ham United?
   A) Alan Pardew B) Gianfranco Zola C) Alan Curbishley
   D) Glenn Roeder

7. West Ham made a terrible start to the 2002/03 season at Upton Park, and their suffering fans had to wait until what number home game before seeing them win?
   A) 11th B) 12th C) 13th D) 14th

8. In July 2017 how much did West Ham pay Stoke City for Marko Arnautovic?
   A) 22 million B) 24 million C) 26 million D) 28 million

9. Which of the following London clubs were the last to make their FA Cup final debut?

   A) Chelsea   B) Spurs   C) West Ham   D) Arsenal

10. What was JD 1226?

   A) The vehicle registration for West Ham's team coach in the 1920s
   B) Julian Dicks's golf club membership number
   C) John Dick's Ladbrokes account number
   D) Jermain Defoe's dog licence number

QUIZ No. 36

POT LUCK

1. Harry Redknapp played 149 league games for West Ham United. Which London club did he play for just once?

2. Which goalkeeper played just once for West Ham in the league in 1968 before playing 471 times for Reading and setting records for clean sheets along the way?

3. Samassi Abou was a player I liked, with the fans making much of his name in games. From which French club did he join West Ham in 1997?

4. Who is the only player to be capped for England while at West Ham and three other London clubs?

5. Many West Ham fans know about the abundance of players with surnames starting with 'B' in the 1960s. There were seven of them in the 1964 FA Cup final. 1965/66 was the zenith for this particular phenomenon. How many players whose names began with that letter represented West Ham in the league that season?

6. Which three surnames have played for and against West Ham in an FA Cup final?

7. Although he didn't get on to the field, who made history in 1975 by being West Ham's first substitute in an FA Cup final?

8. With which London club did West Ham draw 5-5 on 17 December 1966?

9. On 16 April 1965 Brian Dear scored five goals in 20 minutes at Upton Park in a 6-1 league win over which Midlands club?

10. Many Hammers fans know that they lost 8-2 at home to Blackburn Rovers on Boxing Day in 1963. I was there that morning and was very impressed when the West Ham players formed two lines and applauded Blackburn off the pitch. Two days later at Ewood Park, with Rovers on top of the table, the *Daily Mail* produced a cartoon of a programme seller outside Blackburn's ground, saying 'Scorecard, sir' to his customer! West Ham dropped Peters, brought in Bovington to take care of Blackburn's little genius Bryan Douglas, who had run riot at Upton Park, and ran out 3-1 winners. Which West Ham player scored twice in both games?

QUIZ No. 37

SEEING RED

1. Which West Ham player was sent off in different seasons but twice within the calendar year of 2011, the first time in a 2-2 draw at Everton, and the second when the Irons beat Pompey 4-3 at Upton Park?

2. Which West Ham defender received his marching orders at Cardiff City when the Hammers won there 2-0 on 11 January 2014?

3. Which West Ham player got to the dressing room before the other players in the Premier League at Newcastle United in a 0-0 draw on 20 August 2005?

4. Which West Ham player was shown a red card in their 2-0 home defeat at the hands of Manchester United on 2 January 2017 in the Premier League?

5. Who, on 22 December 2012, scored West Ham's goal when they lost 2-1 to Everton at Upton Park before being dismissed by the referee?

6. Which West Ham front man was sent off at Vicarage Road in a 1-1 draw with Watford in the Premier League on 25 February 2017?

7. Which West Ham player was sent off at the Hawthorns in their 4-0 defeat there in the FA Cup fifth round in 2015?

8. Swansea City formed the opposition, going down 2-0 at Upton Park, when which West Ham forward was sent off on 1 February 2014?

9. Which West Ham player was dismissed in the first leg of the League Cup semi-final against Birmingham City at Upton Park on 11 January 2011, a game West Ham won 2-1?

10. Between 4 February and 21 February 2012 a different West Ham player was sent off in three successive Championship fixtures. The culprits were Kevin Nolan, Matt Taylor and Rob Green. The first came in a 2-1 home win, the second in a 1-1 home draw and the last in a 4-1 away win. Which three clubs, one from London, one from the south and one from Lancashire, were they playing?

QUIZ No. 38

TEN TOP HAMMERS – PART 1

1. Which left-sided West Ham defender appeared 248 times in the league for the club and received 17 of his final total of 36 caps for the Republic of Ireland while at the club between 1954 and 1960?

2. Which West Ham favourite, after his second spell up front for the club, became, in season 2000/01, only the second player in history to play in all four divisions in one season?

3. Which member of the 1923 FA Cup final side made exactly 150 league appearances for the Hammers before ending up managing two other London clubs in Crystal Palace and Spurs in the 1930s?

4. A legendary figure at the club between the wars, he averaged more than a goal every two games in his 180 league appearances, leaving just before he would have played in the 1923 final. He did later get his hands on an FA Cup winners' medal when with Blackburn Rovers in 1928 before re-joining West Ham at the end of a career that spanned 20 years. Who was he?

5. Which West Ham player, who made his debut towards the end of the 1961/62 season and made over 300 appearances in the league for the Irons, was unlucky enough to be left out of the 1964 FA Cup-winning side, but made up for it with silverware the next season and something even more significant the following year?

6. This left-winger had an eye for goal and was a big favourite with the Upton Park crowd for almost the entirety of the inter-war years, turning out for the club in the famous FA Cup final of 1923. He was the first West Ham player to break the 500 league appearances barrier and scored over 150 goals for the club. Who was he?

7. It was a gamble when West Ham forked out £430,000 for an uncapped Scot in 1979, but it turned out to be one of the best bargains the club has ever struck. Over a decade and 345 league games later they certainly had their money's worth from this right-sided defender who was probably their best-ever penalty taker. Who was he?

8. Because of the war, this reliable goalkeeper was 25 before he made his West Ham league debut, but that didn't stop him racking up over 400 games in all competitions for the Irons and then going on to be part of the furniture of the place until 1987 in a variety of capacities that he carried out with only one thing on his mind, the welfare of West Ham United. Who was he?

9. A regular goalscorer for West Ham in the drive to get back into the top flight in the late 1950s, scoring over 150 times in 326 league games, he was a member of the Scotland team that faced England at Wembley on the occasion of Billy Wright's 100th international. Who was he?

10. This popular goalscorer was twice signed by West Ham from the North East, firstly from Newcastle United and later from Sunderland. There aren't too many who have scored over 100 goals in all competitions for the club but he did in his two spells in London, the first of which began with a goal on his debut against Nottingham Forest in February 1971 in a 2-0 win. Who was he?

QUIZ No. 39

TEN TOP HAMMERS - PART 2

1. Tony Gale had already played 277 times for Fulham when he joined West Ham in 1984 and added an extra 300 to his total. Which other London club did he play for?

2. Alan Devonshire was a real crowd-pleaser as a creative midfield man between 1976 and 1990, turning out in more than 350 league games for West Ham. Which other club did he play for at the end of his career and which club does he currently manage?

3. Dick Walker played over 300 games in all competitions for West Ham and captained them in the years after World War Two. Some idea of his desire to serve the club can be gleaned from the fact that after his days in the first team ended he turned out over 200 times for the reserves before finally retiring. He was also centre-half in the West Ham team that won the League War Cup final by beating Blackburn Rovers 1-0 in which year?

4. Steve Potts worked his socks off at the back for West Ham over three different decades, clocking up just short of 400 league games for the club. He played 24 times at the end of his career for another club. Which one?

5. George Kay played 237 league games for West Ham at centre-half, and led them out for the 1923 FA Cup final. As a manager, which club did he guide to the league title in the 1940s?

6. Trouble followed defender Julian Dicks around but he was a much-loved figure at Upton Park, and his move to Liverpool was not his idea. In his two spells at West Ham he scored an impressive 50 league goals from the left-back position, but which club did he score just once for in 89 matches?

7. Ted Hufton was a tough character when goalkeepers certainly had to be, and he made over 400 appearances in league football for West Ham, all this coming after being wounded in action in the First World War. He kept goal for the Hammers in the 1923 FA Cup final, and would have played in an FA Cup final eight years before that one had he not suffered a broken nose in an earlier game. That 1915 final was known as the 'Khaki' final. Who would he have played for in it?

8. Rio Ferdinand oozed class at the back for West Ham between 1995 and 2000, playing in 127 league matches for the club. He had all the time in the world on the ball, but which other England centre-half said, 'When I hear about a defender who is good on the ball, I think, "Oh Christ"'?

9. Danny Shea was a goal machine in the Southern League for West Ham, finding the net 111 times in 179 games for them between 1907 and 1913. He then moved north, where his 27 goals in the following season were a significant factor in which club winning the league title?

10. Phil Woosnam was one of West Ham's classiest post-war players and operated at inside-forward for the Irons after they paid £30,000 for him. Which London club did they buy him from, and, being extremely smart with his head as well as his feet, what did he achieve later in life in the football world?

QUIZ No. 40

THAMES IRONWORKS AND WEST HAM UNITED LEAGUE FOOTBALL - 1896-1915

1. Although they were playing in the previous season, Thames
    Ironworks experienced league football for the first time in the
    London League in the 1896/97 season when they finished second.
    The following season they went one better and won that London
    League, losing just one of their 16 games. The club that beat them
    came from west London and finished as runners-up to Thames
    Ironworks, joining them in the Southern League Division 2 for
    season 1898/99. Who were they?

2. Thames Ironworks' first Southern League fixture came on
    10 September 1898, when they won 3-0 away from home on
    the first step on the road to winning it by nine points. The club
    they beat on that first day was the area of London that The Who
    emerged from over 60 years later. Who did West Ham beat?

3. That was the first match taken care of. In the last one on 15 April
    1899 Thames Ironworks won 10-0 at home to a club that has never
    played in the Football League but did take part in the first FA Cup
    season of 1871/72. Who were they?

4. Their fall was dramatic in 1899/1900. Having reached the first
    division of the Southern League they finished second from bottom
    and had to play a 'Test match' against another London club to see
    which of them would have top-flight status the following season.
    The match was played at the newly opened White Hart Lane, with
    West Ham retaining their position in the league with a 5-1 win over
    which club?

5. The new century brought a new name as Thames Ironworks were
    wound up and became West Ham United. They won their first
    game 7-0 on 1 September 1900 against a team from south of the
    river and about 15 miles to the east. Who were they?

6. Which player made his West Ham debut in that game and became their first hat-trick man when he found the net four times?

7. From the beginning of the century until the war, West Ham competed in the first division of the Southern League, finishing no higher than third and no lower than 18th. Which three London clubs, one from the north and two from the west of the capital, won the Southern League over this period?

8. Which exciting player burst upon the scene in the 1908/09 season after a handful of games in the previous season, going on to score over 100 goals in five seasons, and, in 1909/10, scoring four times as many league goals as his nearest West Ham competitor?

9. On 21 October 1911 West Ham met Brentford at Upton Park, with the game producing 11 goals, the most of any league game in this period. What was the score?

10. War brought an end to proceedings and West Ham's final game before the conflict was a 1-1 draw at Upton Park against the most easterly of the Southern League's 20 clubs. Who were they?

QUIZ No. 41

TRANSFERS - 1945-60 - PART 1

The following ten players joined West Ham from one of the ten clubs below. Can you match the player with the club he came from?

1. Mike Grice

2. Eddie Lewis

3. Les Bennett

4. Billy Dare

5. Alan Sealey

6. Harry Kinsell

7. Albert Foan

8. Noel Dwyer

9. Vic Keeble

10. Dave Sexton

Brentford, Colchester United, Leyton Orient, Luton Town, Newcastle United, Norwich City, Preston North End, Reading, Spurs, Wolves.

TRANSFERS - 1945-60 - PART 2

The following ten players left West Ham for one of the ten clubs below. Can you match the player with the club he joined?

1. Jimmy Andrews

2. Derek Parker

3. Sammy Small

4. Harry Hooper

5. John Smith

6. Eric Parsons

7. Frank O'Farrell

8. Ken Tucker

9. Tommy Dixon

10. Gerry Gazzard

Brentford, Brighton, Chelsea, Colchester United, Leyton Orient, Notts County, Preston North End, Reading, Spurs, Wolves.

TRANSFERS - 1960-75 - PART 1

The following ten players joined West Ham from one of the ten clubs below. Can you match the player with the club he came from?

1. Alan Stephenson

2. Peter Brabrook

3. Jim Standen

4. Peter Eustace

5. Ted McDougall

6. Alan Taylor

7. Bobby Gould

8. Graham Paddon

9. Mick McGiven

10. Billy Jennings

Bristol City, Chelsea, Crystal Palace, Luton Town, Manchester United, Norwich City Rochdale, Sheffield Wednesday, Sunderland, Watford.

TRANSFERS - 1960-75 - PART 2

The following ten players left West Ham for one of the ten clubs below. Can you match the player with the club he joined?

1. John Dick

2. Lawrie Leslie

3. Malcolm Musgrove

4. Johnny Byrne

5. Martin Peters

6. Jack Burkett

7. Andy Malcolm

8. Ken Brown

9. Dennis Burnett

10. John Sissons

Brentford, Charlton Athletic, Chelsea, Crystal Palace, Leyton Orient, Millwall, Sheffield Wednesday, Spurs, Stoke City, Torquay United.

TRANSFERS - 1975-90 - PART 1

The following ten players joined West Ham from one of the ten clubs below. Can you match the player with the club he came from?

1. Jimmy Neighbour

2. David Cross

3. Paul Goddard

4. Gary Strodder

5. Mark Ward

6. Tony Gale

7. Trevor Morley

8. Paul Hilton

9. Steve Whitton

10. Dave Swindlehurst

Bury, Coventry City, Derby County, Fulham, Lincoln City, Manchester City, Norwich City, Oldham Athletic, QPR, West Brom.

TRANSFERS - 1975-90 - PART 2

The following ten players left West Ham for one of the ten clubs below. Can you match the player with the club he joined?

1. Gary Lock

2. Alan Curbishley

3. John Radford

4. Derek Hales

5. Paul Brush

6. Steve Walford

7. Keith Robson

8. Paul Allen

9. Alan Dickens

10. Tommy Taylor

Birmingham City, Blackburn Rovers, Cardiff City, Charlton Athletic, Chelsea, Crystal Palace, Fulham, Huddersfield Town, Leyton Orient, Spurs.

QUIZ No. 47

TRANSFERS - 1990-2005 - PART 1

The following ten players joined West Ham from one of the ten clubs below. Can you match the player with the club he came from?

1. Dale Gordon

2. Lee Chapman

3. John Moncur

4. Les Ferdinand

5. David Unsworth

6. John Hartson

7. David James

8. Hayden Mullins

9. Steve Lomas

10. Paulo Wanchope

Arsenal, Aston Villa, Crystal Palace, Derby County, Everton, Glasgow Rangers, Manchester City, Portsmouth, Spurs, Swindon Town.

QUIZ No. 48

TRANSFERS - 1990-2005 - PART 2

The following ten players left West Ham for one of the ten clubs below. Can you match the player with the club he joined?

1. George Parris

2. Alvin Martin

3. Stuart Slater

4. Chris Hughton

5. Leroy Rosenior

6. Martin Allen

7. David Speedie

8. Michael Hughes

9. Paulo Di Canio

10. Trevor Sinclair

Birmingham City, Brentford, Bristol City, Charlton Athletic, Glasgow Celtic, Leicester City, Leyton Orient, Manchester City, Portsmouth, Wimbledon.

QUIZ No. 49

TRANSFERS - 2005-20 - PART 1

The following ten players joined West Ham from one of the ten clubs below. Can you match the player with the club he came from?

1. Ricardo Vaz Te

2. Dean Ashton

3. Jonathan Spector

4. Matthew Upson

5. Kevin Nolan

6. Danny Gabbidon

7. Matt Jarvis

8. Ryan Fredericks

9. Aaron Cresswell

10. Michail Antonio

Barnsley, Birmingham City, Cardiff City, Fulham, Ipswich Town, Manchester United, Newcastle United, Norwich City, Nottingham Forest, Wolves.

TRANSFERS - 2005-20 - PART 2

The following ten players left West Ham for one of the ten clubs below. Can you match the player with the club he joined?

1. Sam Byram

2. Paul Konchesky

3. Andy Carroll

4. James Tomkins

5. Andre Ayew

6. Lee Bowyer

7. Yossi Benayoun

8. Marlon Harewood

9. Anton Ferdinand

10. Matthew Etherington

Aston Villa, Birmingham City, Crystal Palace, Fulham, Liverpool, Newcastle United, Norwich City, Stoke City, Sunderland, Swansea City.

QUIZ No. 51

TRUE OR FALSE

1. The 1960s was the only decade since West Ham's formation when they spent all ten seasons of it in the top flight. True or false?

2. Despite appearing in only half of the League Cup finals that West Ham have been in, Swindon Town, Swansea City, Oxford United and Blackburn Rovers have all won the trophy more times than West Ham. True or false?

3. West Ham were the only side to concede two goals on the day when winning a 1960s FA Cup final. True or false?

4. When West Ham lost the 2006 FA Cup final against Liverpool in a penalty shoot-out, Teddy Sheringham was the only player to be successful from the spot for them. True or false?

5. West Ham have won more home games in a season than all the other clubs in their division while playing in the second tier of English football, but have never done so in any season in the top flight. True or false?

6. Bobby Moore and Scott Parker are the only two players to win the FWA Footballer of the Year award while at West Ham. True or false?

7. Jamie Carragher's own goal against West Ham in the 2006 FA Cup final was the only own goal that assisted a London club in an FA Cup final since the war. True or false?

8. In the 20th century, West Ham have opened a top-flight season after promotion on five occasions, three times at home and twice away. They have won just once on those opening days, at Fratton Park, Portsmouth. True or false?

9. Liam Brady and Frank Lampard Jnr are the only West Ham players to win either Footballer of the Year award while at another London club. True or false?

10. Manchester United and Liverpool were the only other clubs to, like West Ham, win the FA Cup in the 1960s, 1970s and 1980s. True or false?

QUIZ No. 52

VENUES

1. Which is the only ground that West Ham United have won on more than once in an FA Cup semi-final or replay?

2. What is the most northerly ground that West Ham United have played on in an FA Cup semi-final or replay?

3. In which Belgian town did West Ham play their first match in Europe on 23 September 1964?

4. West Ham played on ten Christmas Days after the war but amazingly all of them were at Upton Park! A friendly fixture compiler no doubt. The last away ground West Ham played on on 25 December came in 1936 against a Yorkshire club who haven't played in the league for over 50 years. On which ground did the Hammers lose 2-1 that day?

5. On which club ground did West Ham lose 2-1 to Everton in the 1933 FA Cup semi-final?

6. What was the venue for West Ham's European Cup Winners' Cup final against Anderlecht in 1976?

7. On which club ground in pouring rain did West Ham upset the odds by beating Manchester United 3-1 in the 1964 FA Cup semi-final?

8. West Ham drew 2-2 with Liverpool in the Charity Shield at the start of the 1964/65 season and shared the trophy. Where was the match played?

9. How many FA Cup semi-finals have West Ham played at Villa Park?

10. West Ham have never won the League Cup in any of its ephemeral titles, but they have played in a two-leg final and a one-off affair as well, which went to a replay. Which four grounds were involved in these games?

QUIZ No. 53

WEST HAM UNITED IN THE EUROPEAN CUP WINNERS' CUP - PART 1 - 1964/65 AND 1965/66

1. Who scored West Ham's first goal in Europe when they won 1-0 away to Belgian club La Gantoise on 23 September 1964?

2. In the second leg at Upton Park on 7 October a 1-1 draw was enough to send the Hammers through to the next round. Who had the honour of scoring the first European Upton Park goal for the club?

3. Only one man scored home and away against the same club in the European Cup Winners' Cup of 1964/65. The goals came in a 2-1 away win and a 4-3 home win in round three against Lausanne. Who scored them?

4. Most West Ham fans know that Alan Sealey's two strikes settled the Wembley final in West Ham's favour against TSV Munich 1860, but which was the only other side he scored against in Europe that season?

5. It took West Ham nine matches to win the trophy that year, and Jim Standen kept goal for them in eight of those games. However, injury prevented him playing in the first home game against La Gantoise. Who deputised for him?

6. As holders of the trophy, West Ham entered the competition again in 1965/66 and their first match brought with it their biggest win in the competition over these two seasons. They won 4-0 at Upton Park against which Greek club?

7. They reached the semi-final in that second year, beating a German club to get there but being eliminated by another German club at that stage. Which two German clubs were involved?

8. John Bond, Jack Burkett, Eddie Bovington and Ken Brown all figured for West Ham in the European Cup Winners' Cup in 1964/65. Who was the only one of those four Bs to score?

9. Which Spanish club did West Ham beat 3-2 on aggregate in the semi-final of 1964/65?

10. Which West Ham forward played in all nine games it took to win it but failed to score in any of them? Hard to believe, but true!

QUIZ No. 54

WEST HAM UNITED IN THE EUROPEAN CUP WINNERS' CUP - PART 2 - 1975/76 AND 1980/81

1. West Ham had to travel to Finland and Armenia before they reached the quarter-final of the European Cup Winners' Cup in 1975/76. When they reached that stage, they lost the first leg 4-2 away to which Dutch club?

2. Which player scored both West Ham's goals that night?

3. After an exciting night at Upton Park, West Ham's 3-1 win brought the aggregate score to 5-5. By what method did they progress to the semi-final?

4. Eintracht Frankfurt provided tough opposition in that semi-final but once again, as in every round so far, West Ham were at home in the second leg, and turned a 2-1 deficit into a 4-3 aggregate win. Who scored twice for them in the second leg?

5. Anderlecht, West Ham's opponents in the final, had the distinct advantage of playing in the Heysel Stadium and ran out 4-2 winners. Which player who scored twice for them that night later joined the Hammers?

6. West Ham were in the European Cup Winners' Cup again in 1980/81 and turned around a 1-3 scoreline in Spain in the first leg of their first tie by winning the second leg 5-1 at Upton Park. Who scored West Ham's only European hat-trick of the century in that game and which club did they knock out?

7. What was the attendance that night at Upton Park?

8. Who was the only man to score in the European Cup Winners' Cup for West Ham in both the 1975/76 and 1980/81 seasons?

9. Russian club Dinamo Tbilisi put West Ham out of the competition in 1980/81 after taking the Hammers apart 4-1 in the first leg at Upton Park. To their credit West Ham won the second leg in front of an 80,000 crowd by 1-0. Who became the last West Ham player to score in Europe for them in that century when he got the winner?

10. In their combined European Cup Winners' Cup appearances over the 1960s, 1970s and 1980s, West Ham played in 30 matches. On bonfire night of 1980, what did Romanian side Poli Timisoara do that no other club could?

QUIZ No. 55

WEST HAM IN EUROPE – 1999-2017 - PART 1

1. Which tournament did West Ham United win in the summer of 1999?

2. To reach the final they beat Jokerit and Heerenveen over two legs. Which two countries did those clubs represent?

3. Which French club did they beat 3-1 away in the second leg of the final after losing the first leg 1-0 at Upton Park?

4. Which West Ham player scored against all three clubs?

5. Shortly after that tournament West Ham entered the UEFA cup after a break from European competition of nearly 20 years. They beat Croatian club NK Osijek 6-1 on aggregate in their first tie. Six different players scored the goals. They were Paulo Di Canio, Paulo Wanchope, Frank Lampard, Neil Ruddock, Paul Kitson and another player who sounds like he might play for the opposition! Who was he?

6. West Ham didn't get any further, going out 2-0 on aggregate to a side that won the European Cup in the 1980s. Who were they?

7. Who was the only player to score for the Hammers in the summer tournament of the first question but fail to score for them in the UEFA Cup?

8. West Ham's next experience of European competition came in 2006/07 and lasted half as long as the previous one. Which Italian club beat them 4-0 on aggregate?

9. Who played in goal for West Ham in both matches?

10. A player who scored in the away leg against West Ham joined the club on loan two years later. Who was he?

QUIZ No. 56

WEST HAM IN EUROPE – 1999-2017 – PART 2

1. West Ham had a nine-year wait before they got into Europe again in 2015/16, beating Lusitanos in the first qualifying round by 4-0 on aggregate, before seeing off Birkirkara on penalties after drawing 1-1 on aggregate. Which two countries did those two clubs come from?

2. Which West Ham player had a mixed experience against Lusitanos when he scored twice in the home leg but got a red card away from home in the second?

3. Something similar happened to another West Ham player against Birkirkara in the second qualifying round when he got the 90th-minute winner in the home leg but was sent off in the away leg. Who was he?

4. West Ham found the third qualifying round a bridge too far, going out to Romanian side Astra Giurgiu 4-3 on aggregate. The first leg at Upton Park was drawn 2-2 when yet another West Ham player saw red while another put through his own net. Who were the two players?

5. Which player who shares his name with a Spanish football club scored West Ham's opening goal in that game?

6. Who, by scoring to put West Ham 2-0 up in the 51st minute before they tossed the game away, scored West Ham's last European goal at Upton Park?

7. In the following season West Ham entered the Europa League at the third qualifying round and beat NK Domzale 4-2 on aggregate. In which country were that club situated?

8. When they won the second leg 3-0, which Hammer scored the first goal in European competition at their new ground?

9. They then entered the play-off round, where they came up against the same Romanian side they had met the previous year in the competition, this time going down 2-1 on aggregate to Astra Giurgiu. Who scored from the penalty spot for West Ham in the away legs of both rounds they competed in that year?

10. Astra Giurgiu were therefore the first club to knock West Ham out of Europe in successive seasons, but how many turned up to watch the first leg in Romania?
    A) 3,360 B) 4,360 C) 5,360 D) 6,360

QUIZ No. 57

WEST HAM UNITED IN FA CUP FINALS - PART 1 - CLUBS

1. West Ham United have appeared in five FA Cup finals. Which two of their opponents in those finals had not won the FA Cup when they came out to face West Ham?

2. What is the link between the first three clubs West Ham met in an FA Cup final?

3. What was the year of the only FA Cup final West Ham failed to score in?

4. In what year was West Ham's only experience of extra time in an FA Cup final?

5. How many times have West Ham United won the FA Cup?

6. Who is the only club to currently be on that number with them?

7. The first three decades that West Ham made an FA Cup final appearance in were the 1920s, 1960s and the 1970s. How many other clubs have played in an FA Cup final in each of those decades?

8. Have West Ham United played all five of their FA Cup finals on the same ground? Yes or no?

9. West Ham United won the FA Cup for the first time in the 1960s. Which other club did so as well?

10. In what year was the first FA Cup final that West Ham appeared in that was between two clubs from the same division?

QUIZ No. 58

WEST HAM UNITED IN FA CUP FINALS – PART 2 – PLAYERS

1. Who scored West Ham's first-ever goal in an FA Cup final?

2. Two members of West Ham's losing FA Cup finalists of 1923 shared a surname with two members of their successful FA Cup team of 1964. What were those two surnames?

3. In that 1964 final West Ham created something of a record in that the surnames of their 11 players began with just four letters. What were those four letters?

4. Who are the only two men to score a winning goal in an FA Cup final for West Ham United with their head?

5. Who was the last player to score for West Ham in an FA Cup final?

6. Who is the only player to score twice in an FA Cup final for West Ham?

7. Which West Ham player in the 2006 FA Cup final had previously scored a goal in an FA Cup final?

8. Which West Ham player in the 1980 FA Cup final became the youngest to play in the final of that competition?

9. What is the only surname to appear twice in the same West Ham United FA Cup final line up?

10. Which West Ham player in the 1980 FA Cup final had already scored in an earlier FA Cup final?

QUIZ No. 59

WEST HAM UNITED IN THE FA CUP – 1895-1915

1. As Thames Ironworks they played their first FA Cup tie on 12 October 1895 going down 5-0 away from home. Eight years later as West Ham United they won away to the same club by the same 5-0 scoreline. Who did they play in that first cup tie?

2. Which northern club were the only team to knock West Ham out of the FA Cup three times in this period?

3. Only one club knocked West Ham out on their way to winning the trophy. It happened in the 1912/13 season when West Ham lost 5-0 away from home. Who beat them?

4. The 1912/13 season was the only one in which West Ham played on a neutral ground after two draws against West Brom failed to settle the affair. Which London ground did West Ham emerge the winners from by 3-0?

5. Who scored a hat-trick for West Ham when they beat Preston North End 3-0 at home in the FA Cup in season 1910/11?

6. Only one city outside London had two clubs that both knocked West Ham out of the FA Cup in this period. Which city was it?

7. New Brompton were the penultimate team that Thames Ironworks met in the competition in 1899/1900, and the second club they met in the new century in their new incarnation as West Ham United. What club did New Brompton go on to become?

8. When West Ham beat Rotherham 1-0 in the first round on 11 January 1908, their winning goal was scored by someone who shared his surname with a football club from Lancashire. What was his name?

9. Who scored a hat-trick when West Ham won a replay 3-2 at Clapton Orient on 12 December 1900?

10. On 28 October 1899 in Thames Ironworks' last season before they became West Ham United, they had their record FA Cup win by 7-0 away at the town Mick and Keith grew up in. Who did they beat?

QUIZ No. 60

WEST HAM UNITED IN THE FA CUP – 1919-39

1. In the first season back after the war, West Ham won 6-0 at Upton Park against a Lancastrian club in the second round. This club held the record for the biggest FA Cup final win when they beat Derby County by 6-0 in 1903, until Manchester City equalled it by mauling Watford in 2019. Who did West Ham beat?

2. Another London club were the only FA Cup opponents to put West Ham out of the competition three times in this period. It happened in 1919/20, 1925/26 and 1933/34. Who were they?

3. Although they played in the legendary 1923 FA Cup final, this was not a great time in cup football for the Hammers. In the 1930s they were dumped out at the first hurdle four years in succession. In how many of the 20 seasons covered here did West Ham fail to get past their first opposition?

4. It is relatively rare to go out to the same club by the same score two years running but West Ham managed it when they were beaten 3-1 in 1930/31 and 1931/32. Which London club did the damage?

5. On the way to that first Wembley final of 1923, West Ham knocked out four coastal clubs in a row to reach the semi-final, two from the south coast, one from the north-east and the other from the south-west. Can you name all four?

6. In 1928/29 and 1932/33, West Ham knocked out a famous amateur side. Who were they?

7. The usual suspects of Spurs, Arsenal and Chelsea all beat West Ham in the FA Cup over this period. Who were the only other side from the capital to do so when they won a fourth-round replay 2-0 on their own ground after holding West Ham 1-1 at Upton Park in the 1926/27 season?

8. In the round before in that 1926/27 season West Ham had beaten Spurs 3-2 at home with the help of a hat-trick from which man?

9. West Ham played FA Cup ties on five neutral grounds over this period. In the 1921/22 season after two draws with Swansea Town the authorities chose a ground between the two clubs for the third match that West Ham lost 1-0. Which ground was used?

10. In the last season before the war West Ham's cup exploits threw up an incredible statistic. Their first four games in the competition were played, in that 1938/39 season, on four different grounds in the same city. That city was London. What were the four grounds?

QUIZ No. 61

WEST HAM UNITED IN THE FA CUP – 1945-60

1. This period was not a great one for West Ham in this competition. How many times did they fail to get over the third-round hurdle?

2. It certainly didn't start that way on 5 January 1946, when they thrashed which fellow Londoners 6-0 at Upton Park in the first leg of the third round?

3. Which Lancastrian club were the only one they met three times over these years, beating them in 1951/52 and 1957/58, but going out to them after a replay in 1953/54?

4. West Ham scored five goals away from home just once. It came in the third round of the 1956/57 season when they won 5-3 after a journey to the east of the country. The team they beat did the league double over West Ham that season, but they were no match for them in the cup. Who were they?

5. The only time the Hammers put a decent cup run together came in the 1955/56 season when victories over Preston North End, Cardiff City and Blackburn Rovers brought them an away quarter-final against which London club?

6. The game ended in a 3-3 draw and having done the hard part West Ham couldn't finish the job, going down 2-1 at home in the replay. Who scored a hat-trick for West Ham in the first game?

7. In these 15 seasons, were West Ham ever knocked out of the FA Cup by the eventual winners that year – yes or no?

8. Which player scored a hat-trick for West Ham when they beat Preston North End 5-2 at Upton Park in the FA Cup third round on 7 January 1956?

9. The biggest crowd to watch West Ham in an FA Cup tie in this period was 69,111. On which ground?

10. West Ham's biggest humiliation over this period came on a weekday afternoon on an icy Upton Park pitch on 13 January 1960. They had drawn at Huddersfield on the Saturday and were expected to complete the job at home against the club from a lower division. Things didn't turn out that way and they went down 5-1. Which inspirational manager and young player were the key to this cup shock?

WEST HAM UNITED IN THE FA CUP – THE 1960s

1. This was the decade when West Ham United finally won the FA Cup. In that 1963/64 season, which two London clubs did they beat on their way to winning the trophy?

2. They scored 19 goals in the competition that season and they were scored by just five men. Geoff Hurst, Ronnie Boyce, John Sissons and Johnny Byrne were four of them. Who's missing?

3. Who, in 1964/65, were the only London club to knock West Ham out of the FA Cup in this decade?

4. Which club did West Ham meet in their first match in the FA Cup and the League Cup in the 1961/62 season?

5. Which three clubs beginning with 'S' all put West Ham out of the FA Cup during this decade?

6. In which season did West Ham beat Everton 1-0 in the fifth round and lose to Liverpool by the same score in the next round?

7. The semi-final and final of 1963/64 has been covered elsewhere, but West Ham found themselves 1-0 down at half-time at home to visitors from Lancashire in the quarter-final before turning it around in the second half and running out 3-2 winners. I was there that day and the noise was deafening! Who did they beat?

8. In 1968/69 and 1969/70 the Hammers disappointingly went out of the FA Cup to two teams beginning with 'M'. Who were they?

9. Who scored West Ham United's only hat-trick in the competition in this decade in a 3-3 home draw in the third round on 28 January 1967?

10. Who were West Ham playing that day; a team that won the replay 3-1?

QUIZ No. 63

WEST HAM UNITED IN THE FA CUP – THE 1970s

1. The decade didn't get off to a great start when West Ham went out in the third round by 4-0 at the hands of which Lancastrian club?

2. Worse was to follow. As well as being beaten by the club that would finish bottom of the league that season, news emerged that four players had been at a night club in the early hours the night before the game. Who were the four players?

3. In the following three seasons West Ham went out of the FA Cup at the hands of three teams that all began with the letter 'H'. Who were they?

4. Things picked up considerably after that. So much so that they landed the trophy in 1974/75. In the first two rounds that year they beat their most southerly opposition and their most westerly opposition. Two clubs that also began with the same letter. Who were they?

5. Which four London grounds did they play on to win the FA Cup?

6. West Ham conceded six goals in an FA Cup tie just once in this period. It came on 31 January 1978 in a 6-1 defeat in a fourth-round replay against which club?

7. Which Welsh club from the fourth tier ejected West Ham from the FA Cup by 2-1 in the 1978/79 season?

8. Which was the only ground that West Ham played on more than once in these years in the FA Cup but failed to win on, drawing 0-0 in 1971/72 and losing 2-1 in 1973/74?

9. Who was the only man to score a hat-trick for West Ham in this period, doing so in a fourth-round replay against Hereford United on 14 February 1972?

10. West Ham's FA Cup win in the 1979/80 season is dealt with in the next FA Cup section, but to end let's go back to the cup triumph of 1975. There is a clear pattern concerning their quarter-final win, their semi-final replay win and their win in the final itself. What is that pattern?

QUIZ No. 64

WEST HAM UNITED IN THE FA CUP – THE 1980s

1. The 1980s couldn't have started much better for the Hammers, who got their hands on the trophy again in the first year of the decade. Which club that shares their colours did they knock out on their way to winning it?

2. It was a case of 'after the Lord Mayor's show' for the rest of the decade with West Ham reaching three quarter finals but getting no further. Who, in the 1987/88 season, became the only London club to knock them out of the competition over this decade?

3. Which London club did they have a much better time against, eliminating them from the competition three times in four seasons?

4. Who were the only club that West Ham beat, lost to and drew against in the FA Cup over this period?

5. Which club from Yorkshire knocked West Ham out of the cup in successive seasons in 1985/86 and 1986/87?

6. In the season after winning it and the one following it, West Ham went out of the competition to two clubs beginning with 'W'. Who were they?

7. In 1988/89, West Ham got past Arsenal and Swindon Town after replays which they won 1-0 on each occasion. Which player was responsible for both those winning goals?

8. In 1984/85, two West Ham players scored hat-tricks, the first coming in a 4-1 third-round win over Port Vale, and the second in a 5-1 replay win in the fifth round against Wimbledon. Which two players scored those hat-tricks?

9. Six days into the new decade of the 1990s West Ham made the long journey to Devon for a third round FA Cup tie that they ended up losing 1-0. Who beat them?

10. Twice during this decade West Ham met teams from the same city in successive cup ties. The seasons were 1986/87 and 1987/88. Which two cities were involved?

QUIZ No. 65

WEST HAM UNITED IN THE FA CUP –
THE 1990s

1. At the first hurdle in 1990/91 and 1991/92, West Ham were drawn away to two clubs from Hampshire who both waived their right to home advantage and both drew at Upton Park before going out 6-1 and 1-0 in the replay. Who were the two teams?

2. West Ham encountered non-league opposition again in a 1-0 fifth-round away win in 1993/94, and when they won 2-1 at home in the third round of 1997/98. Which two clubs did they beat?

3. In the fifth round of that 1997/98 campaign, West Ham were involved in their first FA Cup penalty shoot-out when they prevailed 5-4 in that lottery against a club from Lancashire they had drawn with 2-2 at home and 1-1 away. Who were they?

4. Ironically, they lost by the same method after an Upton Park replay in the next round against Arsenal, whose goalkeeper, Alex Manninger, had such a great night that you sensed he'd win the penalty shoot-out as well. Who was West Ham's goalkeeper that night?

5. Which two Welsh clubs defeated West Ham in the FA Cup, the first at Upton Park in a replay in 1996/97, and the second in 1998/99 in an away tie, on both occasions by 1-0?

6. In 1991/92, Sunderland came to Upton Park for a fifth-round replay and ran out 3-2 winners on the road to Wembley in an exciting game. Who scored both of West Ham's goals?

7. West Ham's best run was at the start of the decade in 1990/91 when they reached the semi-final before being put up against it by a poor refereeing decision. In the quarter-final they accounted for Everton 2-1 at Upton Park. Why might Everton have felt particularly depressed about the outcome?

8. Who was the only West Ham player to score in each of the first three seasons of FA Cup football in that decade?

9. Which club did West Ham knock out 5-1 after a 1-1 draw in 1990/91 and then lose to 3-2 after a 0-0 draw in 1993/94?

10. Four clubs who knocked West Ham out of the FA Cup in these years later experienced spells outside the league. Who were they?

QUIZ No. 66

WEST HAM UNITED IN THE LEAGUE – 1919-39

1. West Ham entered the Football League in the first post-war season of 1919/20 and in their second game suffered a 7-0 defeat, a margin of loss they have equalled twice but thankfully never exceeded. This reverse came in Yorkshire, while the second 7-0 came against the eventual champions in 1927/28. Which two clubs inflicted the damage?

2. Which wing-half was a model of consistency, being an ever-present in the league four seasons in a row, starting in 1933/34, and setting a new record for consecutive matches for the club?

3. West Ham's leading goalscorer in the first three post-war seasons also scored their first Football League hat-trick on 7 February 1920 in a 3-1 win at Upton Park. The first letter of his surname is also the first letter of the club he scored three times against. Who was he and who were the opposition that day?

4. Naturally, when West Ham scored seven times in a league game for the first time on the first day of 1921 it was watched by just 8,000 at Upton Park, the lowest crowd of the season. Which Midlands club went home beaten 7-0?

5. 1922/23 was arguably West Ham's finest season. They were promoted and made history by playing in the first Wembley FA Cup final. A week after that final they ran out at Upton Park for their final league game level on points with two Midlands clubs, one of which they were about to play. The Hammers lost 1-0 but went up as runners-up to their conquerors, holding off the other club on goal average, which was helped by West Ham winning 6-0 away to them earlier in the season. Who were the two clubs in this tight finish with West Ham?

6. Which London club were West Ham's first top-flight victims when they lost 1-0 at Upton Park on 27 August 1923? If it helps, the Hammers also beat them 7-0 in 1926/27, a year in which their opponents reached the FA Cup final for the first time.

7. Amateur player Vivian Gibbins scored a hat-trick at Upton Park in a 5-1 win on 11 October 1930 against a northern club that were relegated at the end of that season. Who were they?

8. West Ham went down again in 1931/32 largely through taking just one point from their last ten games. On 5 December 1931, they beat the eventual champions Everton 4-2 at Upton Park when which left-winger, who at the time held the club's appearances record, scored a hat-trick?

9. Things got really ugly in 1932/33 when West Ham escaped a second successive relegation by one point. They clambered to safety by winning their final two home games, beating Spurs 1-0 and another club 3-1, who found themselves going down to the Third Division North as West Ham leapfrogged them to safety. They are the only side that you can sit on and smoke! Who were they?

10. In 1934/35 West Ham missed out on promotion on goal average. Which Lancastrian club beat them 3-1 on 27 April 1935 to secure the second spot when a draw would have been enough to send the Hammers up?

QUIZ No. 67

WEST HAM UNITED IN THE LEAGUE – 1946-60

1. The first ten years or so after the war produced mid-table mediocrity in Division Two for West Ham United, but one player lit up that first season back of 1946/47 when he joined the Hammers from QPR and topped their league goalscoring chart with 15 in just 14 outings. After playing just three times the following season he moved on to Leyton Orient. Who was he?

2. Who was the only West Ham player to score two league hat-tricks for the club with an eight-year gap between them? They came in a 4-0 win over Chesterfield in October 1947 and a 4-0 win over Plymouth in October 1955.

3. On 15 December 1951 Bert Hawkins scored West Ham's only 1950s hat-trick against another London club when they beat which West London team 4-2 at Upton Park – a team that he was shortly to move to?

4. Although goalkeeper Ernie Gregory was the only Hammer to record three ever-present league seasons during this period, only two men managed successive ever-present seasons, the first a winger in the 1940s and the second a wing-half in the 1950s. Who were the two players?

5. Allowing for one season when it was shared, the letter 'D' dominated the surnames of West Ham's top league goalscorer for six successive years starting in 1953/54. Which three players held that honour during that time?

6. A developing tactical understanding behind the scenes led to West Ham leaving their past performances behind in the 1957/58 season when they won the league. They lost just once all season at Upton Park. Which Yorkshire club won there 3-0 on 9 September?

7. A player who turned out on one solitary occasion for West Ham that season on the left wing shared his name with the club that were promoted as runners-up to West Ham. What was his name?

8. West Ham took the first division by storm, winning 2-1 at Portsmouth on the opening day and following up with a 2-0 win over Wolves at Upton Park. Their third match was also at home against Aston Villa. How did that end up?

9. After scoring 101 goals in getting promotion, their 85 in their first season up was a superb effort, enabling a sixth-place finish. In the return against Portsmouth they rattled in six without reply, and when Blackburn Rovers visited on 4 October 1958 they went back on their northern journey beaten 6-3. Who scored four times for West Ham in that game?

10. The 1959/60 season saw them drop eight places in the league and suffer a defeat by 7-0 in Yorkshire that equalled their heaviest margin of defeat in a league game in their history. Who beat them?

QUIZ No. 68

WEST HAM UNITED IN THE LEAGUE – THE 1960s

1. Having got back with the big boys in the late 1950s, West Ham averaged 12th place throughout the 1960s, reaching as high as eighth and as low as 17th. The word that summed them up was unpredictable, and they were involved in some entertaining encounters. One of these came at St. James' Park against Newcastle United on 10 December 1960. How did it end up?

2. Geoff Hurst was their top league goalscorer on six occasions with Johnny Byrne having the accolade twice. Which two West Ham players were top scorers once each, in 1960/61 and 1961/62?

3. Which London club did West Ham beat 6-1 and 7-2 at Upton Park in successive seasons in 1966/67 and 1967/68, the second time contributing to that club's relegation?

4. There were certainly some fireworks at Upton Park on 5 November 1960 when West Ham sent which London club on their short journey home beaten 6-0?

5. There was one club West Ham really enjoyed playing in the early 1960s. Having won 5-3 away to them in 1961/62 as a warm-up, they beat them 6-1 home and away in 1962/63. Who were they?

6. Which Midlands club did West Ham beat 5-0 at Upton Park two seasons in a row in 1962/63 and 1963/64?

7. In 1964/65, in line with their entertaining image, West Ham equalled their club record in league football by drawing just four of their 42 matches. The four draws came in just two cities. Which two?

8. Four years later in 1968/69 they went to the other extreme, setting a new club record for the most draws in a season. How many of their 42 games finished level?

9. Christmas in 1967 brought a Midlands club to Upton Park on Boxing Day with the reciprocal fixture coming on the 30th. West Ham won both games 4-2 against which opponents?

10. The one and only Jimmy Greaves kept up his record of scoring in every debut throughout his distinguished career when he found the net in his first game for West Ham in a 5-1 away win on 21 March 1970. Who did they beat?

QUIZ No. 69

WEST HAM UNITED IN THE LEAGUE – THE 1970s

1. West Ham's longest run in the top flight in their history finally came to an end in 1977/78, when they fell victim to the change in the rules that came into place five years before that introduced an extra relegation place beyond the traditional two. It was unfortunate that they had to play Liverpool at Upton Park on the final day because they had battled hard in winning six of their eight previous games to give themselves a chance. The run began on 24 March 1978 when three goals by which player enabled them to win 3-0 at home to Ipswich Town?

2. Who was the only West Ham player to score in the league for them in all ten seasons of the decade?

3. Which West Ham defender was the only player to be ever-present in the league in three seasons in the decade?

4. Apart from 1972/73 when they finished sixth, things had been trending downward in this decade although only one club beat them 6-0 in these years. It came away from home on 5 March 1977. Who beat them?

5. Which West Ham player scored a hat-trick in a 3-1 win over Stoke City on 20 December 1975 at Upton Park?

6. West Ham, in the middle of the decade, twice rattled in five goals away from home in the league against two clubs beginning with the same letter. They won 5-3 in Lancashire in September 1974 and 5-1 in the Midlands in November 1975. Which two clubs did they beat?

7. West Ham found it a bit easier to score in Division Two, which was where they found themselves for the 1978/79 season. In that season, they scored five times in the league at Upton Park on three occasions, beating league football's oldest existing club, a club that shares that club's colours, and a team from a city with a world-famous university. Which three clubs did they put five past?

8. It was a real struggle to get back up again but it looked likely for a while in that 1978/79 season until they won just one of their last seven games. After finishing fifth that season they fell to seventh in 1979/80, but only one club did the league double over them. That club entered the league in 1950 and have never played in the top flight, having spent all but ten years in the bottom two divisions. They beat West Ham 3-0 on their ground and 3-1 at Upton Park, Who were they?

9. Who, with ten league goals, was West Ham's top scorer in their relegation season of 1977/78?

10. Geoff Hurst scored his last league hat-trick for West Ham on 3 October 1970 at Upton Park against which Lancastrian club?

QUIZ No. 70

WEST HAM UNITED IN THE LEAGUE – THE 1980s

1. 1980/81 saw West Ham storm to the Division Two title by 13 points with just four defeats along the way. The last of these came on Boxing Day away to another London club by 3-0. Who were they?

2. In April that season David Cross scored four times in a 5-1 away win on West Ham's most easterly away trip. Then, back in the top flight in September, he repeated the trick much closer to home in a 4-0 away win against another London club. Which two clubs did he despatch with those eight away strikes?

3. Before that September was over another West Ham player had recorded a hat-trick against Southampton at Upton Park in a 4-2 win. Who was he?

4. West Ham scored five goals just once in the 1983/84 season and they came in a 5-2 home win over Coventry City on 10 September. Steve Whitton got two of them, but who scored the other three?

5. Just when it looked like trouble might be around the next bend, West Ham produced a massive leap forward in 1985/86 to record their best top-flight finish in their entire history. When they played their last league game away from home a win could have brought the trophy back to Upton Park providing another result went their way as well. In the event, Liverpool won the league and West Ham were denied second spot by losing 3-1 to the team that leap-frogged them into that position. Who were they?

6. After all the promise of 1985/86 the goals started to dry up as the Hammers finished 15th and 16th before relegation loomed again. However, 1986/87 did produce a 5-3 win over Chelsea and a fourth brilliant season in a row from Tony Cottee, who scored away hat-tricks at a Midlands ground and a London ground that both have 'Road' in their name. Which two grounds were they?

7.   Thirty-seven goals are not going to keep you up and West Ham found this out the hard way in 1988/89. The only silver lining came in the name of one of the two clubs West Ham did the league double over. Newcastle United were one of them. Who was the other?

8.   Back in Division Two, when it sensibly still went under that title, West Ham scored more than twice as many goals as the previous season but couldn't finish higher than seventh. In fact, they scored more goals than the champions that season. Who were they?

9.   Cottee, Cross, McAvennie and Goddard shared the first eight seasons as top league goalscorer with the first mentioned landing four of them. Which two players won the last two of the decade?

10. Let's end with that great 1985/86 season. Four players were on the field in all their 42 league games: a goalkeeper, a defender, a combative midfielder and a front man. Who were the four?

QUIZ No. 71

WEST HAM UNITED IN THE LEAGUE – THE 1990s

1. West Ham regained their top-flight status and would have gone up as champions if they had beaten Notts County at Upton Park on the last day. Who were the champions and which club did the Hammers beat 7-1 on 6 October 1990?

2. In true 'Snakes and Ladders' fashion, West Ham were relegated again in 1991/92 with the same number of goals and points as on the previous occasion. A certain madness accompanied their downfall as they were relegated from Division One into Division One! This was of course due to the rebranding that produced the Premier League and wrecked all meaningful comparison from that point on. When it was all too late West Ham came alive on 2 May 1992 when which player bagged a hat-trick as Forest went down 3-0 on the last day of the season at Upton Park?

3. They didn't take long getting back with the big boys, who were increasingly perceived as having found the Holy Grail. They won their last four games, the final one producing a 2-0 win at Upton Park through goals by David Speedie and Clive Allen. Who did they beat, which club did they ease out of an automatic promotion place on goal difference, and which club won the league?

4. In 1993/94 West Ham finished 13th in the Premier League. Which midfielder scored in all the last five games that season that West Ham scored in?

5. The following season saw them finish around the same position but they were very much involved in the excitement at the season's end concerning the destination of the title. Some great goalkeeping by Miklosko saw Manchester United held 1-1 at Upton Park with the Premier League trophy going to Blackburn Rovers. Which West Ham player scored the vital goal?

6. West Ham were involved in a controversial situation when the Upton Park lights failed with their game against Crystal Palace poised at 2-2 on 3 November 1997. The circumstances were mysterious and the game was declared void. West Ham won the rematch 4-1 exactly one month later. Which West Ham man scored in both games?

7. In that 1997/98 season, West Ham won 2-1 away on the opening day and beat the same side 6-0 in the return at Upton Park in January. This was to be their only top-flight season in the history of the club. Who were they?

8. What a topsy-turvy world. West Ham scored just 46 goals yet finished fifth. They lost 6-0 at Everton in the season's penultimate game, and then beat Middlesbrough 4-0 in the final one. Before that they won and lost successive games at Upton Park 5-1 against two clubs who were involved in a few battles in the 1970s. Who were they?

9. In the final season of the decade, West Ham scored six more goals and dropped four places. Upton Park was treated to a breath-taking goal from Paulo Di Canio against Wimbledon but six days later West Ham lost away 7-1. Who beat them?

10. Which West Ham player was their leading league goalscorer in three of the first four years of the decade?

QUIZ No. 72

WEST HAM UNITED IN LEAGUE CUP FINALS AND SEMI-FINALS – PART 1 – CLUBS

1. West Ham have played in nine League Cup semi-finals but have never met any team twice at that stage of the competition. True or false?

2. In sharp contrast to their record in FA Cup semi-finals where they have won five out of seven, in League Cup semi-finals they have progressed to the final just twice in nine attempts. These semi-final wins came in 1966 and 1981 and were achieved against two 'City' teams whose names begin with the same letter. Who were they?

3. In 1989 and 2014 West Ham failed to score in either leg of their League Cup semi-finals, going down 5-0 and 9-0 on aggregate to which two clubs?

4. Who are the only club that have beaten West Ham in a League Cup final and a League Cup semi-final?

5. Which two clubs have beaten West Ham 6-0 in the first leg of a League Cup semi-final?

6. In 1972 West Ham were involved in four matches to decide their League Cup semi-final against which club?

7. Which Midlands club knocked out West Ham in the League Cup semi-final of 1964 on their way to winning the trophy?

8. In 2011 West Ham lost a great chance to play in another League Cup final when they held a two-goal lead at half-time in the away second leg of the semi-final. However, they contrived to lose the tie in extra time against a team whose own fans had booed them off at half-time. Who were they?

9. Who are the only club to concede ten goals to West Ham over two legs in a League Cup semi-final?

10. Who are the only club West Ham have lost to in both a League Cup final and an FA Cup final?

QUIZ No. 73

WEST HAM UNITED IN LEAGUE CUP FINALS AND SEMI-FINALS – PART 2 – PLAYERS

1. West Ham United lost 5-3 on aggregate in their first League Cup final of 1966. Which three England internationals scored their goals?

2. Who is the only player to score for West Ham in a League Cup final at Wembley?

3. Who scored for West Ham in both the League Cup semi-final and the League Cup final replay in 1981?

4. Who was the only man to score for West Ham United in the League Cup semi-finals of 1964, 1966, 1967 and 1972?

5. In 1990 West Ham won a second leg semi-final 3-0 at Upton Park but it was a case of too little too late. Who scored from the penalty spot for West Ham that night?

6. Which West Ham forward scored home and away when they lost 4-3 on aggregate in the League Cup semi-final of 2011?

7. In the away second leg, which West Ham lost 3-1 in extra time, which ex-Hammer scored a vital goal against his old club?

8. West Ham United have had just one 2-2 draw in all the 24 matches they have contested in League Cup finals and semi-finals. It came in the home second leg in 1967 when Byrne and Hurst scored their goals. Who were they playing?

9. West Ham were unlucky to go out in the League Cup semi-final of 1972 when in the second leg at Upton Park the visitor's goalkeeper made a great penalty save from Geoff Hurst to stop his side going two down. Another goalkeeper was involved in the fourth game but was concussed and had to leave the field. Who were these two goalkeepers?

10. In that game who went in goal for West Ham and saved a penalty, only for their opponents to score from the rebound?

QUIZ No. 74

WEST HAM UNITED IN THE LEAGUE CUP – THE 1960s

1. This new cup competition launched in the 1960/61 season was often seen as the FA Cup's ugly cousin, and although West Ham, over 60 years later, have still not got their hands on the trophy, they have been involved in some epic encounters over the years. The very first draw paired them with another London club that they beat 3-1 at Upton Park on 26 September 1960 in front of just 12,000 fans. Who did they beat?

2. In 1961/62 and 1962/63 they were knocked out by the two teams that contested the first final in the competition in 1960/61. Who were those two teams?

3. West Ham enjoyed big home wins in 1962/63 against Plymouth Argyle and in the following season against Workington. The score was the same in both games. What was it?

4. One West Ham player had a field day in those two matches, registering a hat-trick in both of them. Who was he?

5. West Ham went all the way to the final in 1965/66, but needed replays on two occasions, one against a side from the west of the country and the other against a side from the east. Who were the two teams?

6. West Ham had another good stab at it the next season as well, this time reaching the semi-final stage. After pleasing their supporters by eliminating Spurs and Arsenal, they then turned on the style in the next round at Upton Park when they beat which club 7-0?

7. Two players scored hat-tricks in that game. Who were they?

8. Who was the only player to score for West Ham United in all the first three years of the new competition?

9. Which Lancastrian club lost 4-1 and 7-2 in the League Cup in 1967/68 and 1968/69 at Upton Park against West Ham?

10. This club weren't the only one to be knocked out of the competition in successive seasons by West Ham. Which club from the west of the country suffered the same fate in 1961/62 and 1962/63?

QUIZ No. 75

WEST HAM UNITED IN THE LEAGUE CUP
- THE 1970s

1. I thought we would start this section with a bit of poetry. Why not, I hear you shout! Philip Larkin, that great lover of humanity and family, worked for many years in the north-eastern city that West Ham beat 1-0 with a Peter Eustace goal in their first League Cup fixture of the 1970/71 season. In the next round they were knocked out 3-1 in the Midlands city of his birth. Which were the two clubs West Ham played in that season's League Cup?

2. Three times over the decade, West Ham's exit from the competition came at the hands of fellow Londoners, two from the west of the capital and one from the north. Which three clubs were involved?

3. In 1977/78, and again two years later, a Midlands club put West Ham out of the competition, scoring eight goals without reply in the three games they met in. Who were they?

4. West Ham enjoyed a run to the semi-final in 1972 and that four-match epic has been dealt with elsewhere. They needed replays to get past their first two opponents that season, namely Cardiff City and Leeds United. What was surprising about their progress past those two clubs?

5. After then accounting for Liverpool in that season, they thrashed Sheffield United 5-0 in the Upton Park quarter final. Who scored a hat-trick in that game?

6. Which club from the west of the country did West Ham eliminate from the competition in 1972/73 and again in 1975/76?

7. They scored six goals in a League Cup tie just once. It came in a 6-0 home win over a team from the North West in the 1974/75 season after they had taken West Ham to a replay with a 0-0 draw at their place. Who were they?

8. A West Ham player scored a hat-trick in that game and five years later another player, who scored three of his four goals for the club in one evening, did the same when Southend were finally overcome at the third time of asking 5-1 at Upton Park. Who were these two scorers of hat-tricks, the second of which was the son of a West Ham player?

9. Which full-back scored his first West Ham goal in a 2-1 win over Bristol City on 6 September 1972?

10. West Ham were vulnerable to lower division opposition in this competition and went out in 1972/73 and 1978/79 to two clubs below them in the pecking order whose names began with 'S'. Who were they?

WEST HAM UNITED IN THE LEAGUE CUP
- THE 1980s

1. After coming close to winning it at the start of the decade, West Ham reached two more semi-finals at the end of it, only to be bitterly disappointing both times. Who were the only club to knock them out of the competition twice in this period, with the silver lining being that the Hammers also defeated them as well?

2. Which Midlands club did West Ham play six games against in the League Cup over this time, winning four of them and drawing the other two?

3. On West Ham's road to the final of 1980/81, there was only one occasion when one of their players scored twice in a game. It came in a 2-1 win at Charlton Athletic on 23 September 1980. Who bagged the two goals?

4. Which West Ham player scored two of the goals when they beat Liverpool 4-1 on a great night at Upton Park on 30 November 1988?

5. Which London club did West Ham beat on the way to the 1981 final, but lose heavily to after a replay in the 1986/87 competition?

6. In the successive seasons of 1984/85 and 1985/86, West Ham went out of the competition to two teams from the same city. Which one?

7. The biggest win in the history of the club came in this decade in this competition. Which club went down 10-0 at Upton Park on 25 October 1983?

8. Tony Cottee scored four times in that game and three years later notched up another hat-trick in a 4-1 second leg win against which club from Lancashire at Upton Park?

9. Francois Van der Elst got in on the hat-trick stakes when he scored all three of West Ham's goals in a 3-3 away draw in the Midlands on 7 December 1982. West Ham won the replay 3-0. Who were their opponents?

10. In the 1989/90 season, West Ham's first two opponents were deadly rivals from the same city. West Ham accounted for both of them, the first 3-2 on aggregate and the second by 1-0 at Upton Park after a 0-0 away draw. Which city was it?

QUIZ No. 77

WEST HAM UNITED IN THE LEAGUE CUP – THE 1990s

1. West Ham reached just one quarter-final in the League Cup in this decade and they lost at the same stage on the same ground to the same team in the same season in the FA Cup as well. Who beat them?

2. Which future West Ham manager saved their blushes on 25 September 1996 by scoring the only goal of the game to beat Barnet in the second leg of the second round, the first leg having been drawn 1-1?

3. Two teams with 11 letters to their name and nine of those letters in common knocked West Ham out of the League Cup, the first in 1995/96 and the second in 1998/99. Who were the two teams?

4. In 1997/98 two West Ham players registered hat-tricks in the League Cup, both of them coming at Upton Park. The first was in a 3-0 win over Huddersfield Town, and the second in a 4-1 win over Walsall. Who were the two players?

5. On 26 October 1994, West Ham fans had the pleasure of a 1-0 home win over Chelsea in the competition. Whose goal proved to be the decider?

6. West Ham found the net five times on just one occasion over the decade. It came in a 5-1 home win in the first leg of the second round on 22 September 1993, when Morley, Chapman and Burrows shared the goals. Who did they beat?

7. In 1991/92, after putting out Bradford City and Sheffield United, the Hammers succumbed 2-1 at Norwich City. Which player scored half of the eight goals they managed in the competition that year?

8. Which Midlands club did West Ham lose to 2-1 in 1993/94 away from home, but beat 4-1 at Upton Park in 1996/97?

9. West Ham were in a great mood after reaching the semi-final stage in 1999/2000 via a penalty shoot-out at Upton Park after a 2-2 draw. That mood soon changed when it transpired that Manny Omoyinmi was ineligible for the match and it had to be replayed. Naturally, West Ham lost the second encounter 3-1. Who beat them?

10. A tough one to finish with. Who, in 1996/97, was the only West Ham player to score in both domestic cup competitions?

QUIZ No. 78

WEST HAM UNITED IN OTHER COMPETITIONS

1. On 8 June 1940, in the week of the Dunkirk evacuation, West Ham won the first League War Cup final in front of over 42,000 at Wembley by beating which northern club 1-0 through a Sammy Small goal?

2. Which is the only club West Ham have beaten and lost to in an FA Youth Cup final, the win coming in 1963 and the loss in 1996?

3. The first time that West Ham entered the Southern Floodlight Cup in 1955/56, they won it, but it took just three matches and they beat Aldershot 2-1 in the final at Upton Park. The only other time they went close was in 1959/60, when they reached the final after knocking out Millwall, Reading, Leyton Orient and Arsenal to get there. Which Midlands club beat them 2-1 in the final?

4. West Ham have played in three Charity Shields. Two of them in 1964 and 1980 involved Liverpool. Who was the other one against when the Hammers went down 2-0 in 1975?

5. West Ham played three matches in the Texaco Cup in August of 1974, losing to Luton Town and Southampton after beating which fellow Londoners?

6. West Ham's only game in the Watney Cup came on 11 August 1973 when they lost on penalties after a 1-1 away draw to which club from the west country in front of a 20,000 crowd?

7. Between 1985 and 1992, West Ham entered a competition that started out as the Full Members' Cup. They reached the semi-final in 1992, by which time it was called the Zenith Data Systems Cup. But before that, when it was known as the Simod Cup, on 9 November 1988, they beat West Brom 5-2 at Upton Park in the competition. Who scored four of those five goals?

8. The Anglo-Italian Cup Winners' Cup was a strange event that West Ham played in in September and December of 1975 as the English FA Cup winners. They lost 1-0 home and away to which Italian club?

9. Not to be confused with the subject of the previous question, the Anglo-Italian Cup was a competition West Ham entered in 1992 with Bristol Rovers, Southend United and three Italian clubs. The Italians clearly had better things to do than watch this spectacle, because when West Ham won 1-0 away to Cozenza on 8 December 1992 the crowd was somewhat sparse. What was the attendance?
A) 600   B) 700   C) 800   D) 900

10. Spare a thought for this guy. He had played just six games for West Ham when war broke out. Representing West Ham in the Regional Leagues during the conflict, he scored 154 goals in 179 games, but they don't appear in most of the record books. He shares his name with a world heavyweight champion boxer. Who was he?

QUIZ No. 79

WEST HAM UNITED - SEASON 2000/01

1. West Ham finished 15th in the Premier League this season. Who was the club's leading goalscorer in the league and the FA Cup, with 11 in the former and three in the latter?

2. West Ham fans love a spirited comeback against a club they don't care for overmuch and there are a few of these! Which club did they trail to by 2-0 on 26 August 2000 at Upton Park before a Paulo Di Canio penalty in the 86th minute and a Davor Suker goal in the 89th got them an unlikely point?

3. Which Midlands club, who were promoted out of the third tier of English football via the play-offs that season, did West Ham knock out of both domestic cup competitions?

4. After accounting for that club in the League Cup, West Ham beat Blackburn Rovers 2-0 at Upton Park in the next round before going out to which Yorkshire club on the same ground by 2-1 in the following round?

5. When West Ham lost 2-0 at home to Sunderland on 13 January 2001, which man who was a Hammer before and after that season got one of the visitors' goals that day?

6. On 12 February 2001 West Ham led Coventry City 1-0 going into injury time at Upton Park when which player was unfortunate enough to equalise for Coventry with an own goal?

7. Two players who shared a surname played in 49 league matches between them over the season. Who were they?

8. Which Everton player who would later join the Hammers scored from the penalty spot against them at Upton Park on 31 March 2001 when the Merseysiders won 2-0?

9. Which West Ham player received a red card when they lost 1-0 at home to Leicester City on 23 August 2000?

10. Which player scored West Ham's last FA Cup goal of the season when they went down 3-2 at home to Spurs in the quarter-final, and also scored their last Premier League goal in a 2-1 defeat at Middlesbrough on the season's final day?

QUIZ No. 80

WEST HAM UNITED - SEASON 2001/02

1. West Ham improved to occupy seventh place in the Premier League after one of those rare seasons when the home form and away form are exact opposites, West Ham winning 12, drawing four, and losing three at home while winning three, drawing four and losing 12 away. Which defender missed just three league games?

2. The Hammers suffered what may well be the two worst back-to-back league results in their history. On 29 September and 14 October, they travelled north and lost 5-0 and 7-1, scoring two own goals in the process. No other club conceded seven goals in the Premier League that season. Which two clubs hammered them, so to speak?

3. The same player as the previous year topped the goalscoring for West Ham in the Premier League and also scored the same number of goals as the 11 of the previous season. Who was, with ten, the only other Hammer to reach double figures in the league?

4. It was galling to go out of the FA Cup to Chelsea in the fourth round at home after bringing them back to Upton Park. Which club from the fourth tier of English football had they beaten 3-0 away in the third round?

5. West Ham went down the M4 for their first League Cup tie of the season and it proved to be their last! After a 0-0 draw they went out 6-5 on penalties to which club?

6. West Ham didn't have far to go for their most exciting game of the season on 19 November 2001 when they drew 4-4 with which club?

7. Which West Ham player scored a hat-trick in that game?

8. Five days later which Spurs player who later joined West Ham got the only goal of the game at Upton Park when the teams met?

9. On which ground did Jermaine Defoe make the away fans very happy indeed with the only goal of the game on 8 December 2000?

10. Which player scored two vital 89th-minute goals for West Ham, the first being the equaliser at White Hart Lane in April, and the second being the winner at Upton Park on the final day of the season against Bolton Wanderers?

QUIZ No. 81

WEST HAM UNITED - SEASON 2002/03

1. After ten years at the top table West Ham were relegated after a season in which they didn't win at home before Christmas and their leading goalscorer failed to reach double figures. Whose nine goals were good enough to win the award?

2. Which two players, although they didn't start every game, were nevertheless on the pitch at some stage of every one of the 38, scoring eight times each into the bargain?

3. After scraping through on penalties at Chesterfield in the League Cup, which Lancastrian club from two divisions below knocked West Ham out 1-0 at Upton Park in the next round?

4. It's best to draw a veil after West Ham's exit in the fourth round of the FA Cup at Old Trafford, but in the third round on 4 January 2003 they beat Nottingham Forest 3-2 at Upton Park, where one of the visitors' goals was scored by someone who would soon become a Hammer. Who was he?

5. Why were the West Ham fans singing 'fortune's always hiding' – not strictly accurate – when the Hammers lost 2-0 at home to Charlton Athletic on 31 August 2002?

6. When Spurs and West Ham met at White Hart Lane on 15 September 2002 one of the Spurs goals was scored by someone who would eventually join West Ham, and one of the West Ham goals was scored by someone who would eventually sign for Spurs. Who were the two players?

7. Who was the only West Ham player to score for the club in both domestic cup competitions?

8. On the season's opening day West Ham lost 4-0 at Newcastle United, where one of the home side's goals was scored by someone who would end up at West Ham. Who was he?

9. On 11 January 2003 West Ham came up against Newcastle United again at Upton Park in a game that ended 2-2, and again one of Newcastle's goals came from a player who would wind up at the Hammers. Who was he this time?

10. When things looked hopeless West Ham found three 1-0 wins in a row and gave themselves a chance on the final day of avoiding going down with West Brom and Sunderland who had long been cut adrift. They had to do better than Bolton to survive, but Bolton won and West Ham drew 2-2 away with which club and were relegated?

QUIZ No. 82

WEST HAM UNITED - SEASON 2003/04

1. West Ham finished fourth in the First Division, a ridiculous title because it wasn't! In the play-off semi-final which club did they beat 2-1 on aggregate after losing the first leg 1-0?

2. They went into the play-off final as favourites but lost 1-0 to which club?

3. Which defender was the only man to play in 40 of the 46 league games?

4. Who scored a hat-trick when West Ham beat Wimbledon 5-0 on 9 March 2004?

5. West Ham were knocked out of the FA Cup by a London club, and another London club did for them in the League Cup. These two teams share the same colours. Who were they?

6. Which Yorkshire club did West Ham draw 3-3 with away from home on 17 January 2004?

7. Against which club did Jermain Defoe grab a hat-trick on 23 September in a 3-2 away win in the League Cup?

8. Which ex-Hammer scored both goals when Reading beat West Ham 2-0 on 3 April 2004 at the Madejski Stadium?

9. Which West Ham player had a rather eventful day against West Brom at Upton Park on 8 November 2003 when he scored two of the goals that gave the Hammers a 3-0 lead before putting through his own goal in a second half that saw West Ham lose the game 4-3?

10. Who, with 13 goals, was their top goalscorer in the league?

QUIZ No. 83

WEST HAM UNITED - SEASON 2004/05

1. Despite finishing a massive 21 points behind the champions, West Ham achieved their aim of promotion to the Premier League through the play-offs. Who were those champions?

2. On the season's final day, West Ham and Reading were level on points in their quest for sixth spot and a play-off place. Reading lost at Wigan and West Ham won 2-1 away to which club to get themselves over the line?

3. Which West Ham defender picked a timely moment to score his only goal of the league season in that game?

4. Ipswich Town provided the opposition for the play-off semi-final for the second successive year, but couldn't stop the Hammers reaching the final where they won 1-0 against which club?

5. Bobby Zamora scored in all three play-off matches. True or false?

6. The two clubs that knocked West Ham out of the domestic cup competitions had met each other in the 1915 FA Cup final. Who were they?

7. West Ham's top league goalscorer with 20 to his name was also voted the Championship's Player of the Season. Who was he?

8. Crewe Alexandra escaped relegation by one goal but scored more goals at home than promoted West Ham. 19 February saw their only big win at Upton Park and it came against Plymouth Argyle. What score did they win by?

9. It was a season when ex-Hammers regularly came back to haunt the club. Jodie McAnuff, Paul Ince, David Connolly and Dave Kitson, yet again with a hat-trick, all got in on the act. Which four clubs were they playing for?

10. Another goalscorer against West Ham went on to join them. He got both Crewe goals on 21 August 2004 when West Ham won 3-2 at Gresty Road. Who was he?

QUIZ No. 84

WEST HAM UNITED - SEASON 2005/06

1. West Ham finished ninth in the Premier League but the big story was their run to the FA Cup final in which they came agonisingly close to winning the trophy. Which club did they play in both domestic cup competitions, beating them in the FA Cup and losing to them in the League Cup?

2. Who was on the pitch for West Ham in 37 of their 38 league games and was also their top league goalscorer with a total of 14?

3. The first two clubs to make their exit from the FA Cup at the hands of West Ham were Norwich City, who lost 2-1 on their own ground, and Blackburn Rovers, who went down 4-2 at Upton Park. Which player scored in both those games for the Hammers?

4. Against which club did Marlon Harewood score a Premier League hat-trick in a 4-0 win at Upton Park on 12 September 2005?

5. Whose two goals away to Manchester City in the FA Cup quarter-final on 20 March 2006 put West Ham into the semis?

6. Who scored for Bolton Wanderers in their 2-1 win at West Ham on 27 August 2005 before eventually joining the Londoners?

7. Which Blackburn Rovers player who found the net when his team were beaten in the FA Cup fourth round at Upton Park later became a Hammer?

8. Which West Ham player was extremely unlucky to miss out on the FA Cup final when he was sent off for a fairly innocuous incident in the league game between West Ham and Liverpool at Upton Park on 26 April 2006?

9. Which ex-Hammer came back to Upton Park and scored one of the goals by which Portsmouth beat West Ham 4-2 on 18 March 2006?

10. The season's final game produced no little excitement and controversy at Upton Park when West Ham dashed Spurs' hopes of a Champions League place by winning 2-1 and handing the spot to Arsenal instead. Spurs wanted the game replayed because several of their players were ill before the match, but didn't get a decision in their favour. What has the incident come to be known as, and which ex-Hammer scored the Spurs goal that day?

QUIZ No. 85

WEST HAM UNITED - SEASON 2006/07

1. If you score less than a goal a game in the league you are likely to struggle, and West Ham finished in 15th place. Who started 35 of their 38 league games?

2. In the two domestic cup competitions West Ham beat just one club in a complete turnaround from the season before. They won 3-0 at home in the FA Cup third round against which southern club?

3. Which club put an end to dreams of another FA Cup run by winning 1-0 at Upton Park in the fourth round?

4. Bonfire night was a bit special at Upton Park when Marlon Harewood struck in the 90th minute to score the game's only goal against which fellow Londoners?

5. On 7 April 2007, West Ham completed the double over the same club when they won by the same score of 1-0 away from home. Whose goal was the clincher?

6. Perhaps the worst performance of the season came at Reading on New Year's Day when West Ham lost by what score?

7. West Ham's season in the League Cup lasted just one game at Chesterfield where they were beaten 2-1. Who therefore became their only scorer in that competition for the season?

8. A poor season did have its moments, especially on 17 December 2006 when they entertained Manchester United at Upton Park and won 1-0. Who scored the second-half winner?

9. Then on the final day of the season they went to Old Trafford and beat them again by the same score, although it has to be said that Manchester United didn't have anything to play for having already won the league. Who scored West Ham's winner?

10. By far the most irritating moment of the season came on the night of 4 March 2007 when West Ham went 3-2 up at Upton Park in the 85th minute through a Zamora goal against Spurs, only to concede two goals in a minute at the death and lose the game 4-3. What was the half-time score in the game?

QUIZ No. 86

WEST HAM UNITED - SEASON 2007/08

1. In an injury ravaged season West Ham could be pleased with their tenth-place finish, but there was some unrest along the way when between 1 March and 9 March they managed to lose by the same score to Chelsea, Liverpool and Spurs. What was that score?

2. Rob Green was Hammer of the Year and never missed a league game between the posts, but which other defender was also an ever-present for those 38 Premier League games?

3. Which new signing scored the two goals by which West Ham beat Bristol Rovers 2-1 at the Memorial Ground in the League Cup on 28 August 2007?

4. West Ham's biggest win of the season came away from home by 5-0 against a club who won just once all season. Who were they?

5. The two clubs who ended West Ham's hopes in the two domestic cup competitions met each other in the 1933 FA Cup final. Who were they?

6. The West Ham fans who made the long journey to Middlesbrough on 22 December 2007 were treated to an early Christmas present when which midfielder grabbed a 90th-minute winner for the Hammers?

7. Who was West Ham's top league goalscorer with ten to his name?

8. Which three players with the same surname scored either for or against West Ham in the Premier League during the season?

9. Which two defenders scored the goals that sent Manchester United away from Upton Park beaten 2-1 on 29 December 2007?

10. The record Premier League crowd for the season of 76,013 was set on the last day at Old Trafford when West Ham were the visitors, going down 4-1. Which two ex-Hammers were among the scorers?

QUIZ No. 87

WEST HAM UNITED - SEASON 2008/09

1. West Ham experienced financial problems, had Alan Curbishley resign and Gianfranco Zola take over as manager and managed to finish the Premier League season in ninth place. It had all started back on 16 August 2008 with a 2-1 home win over Wigan Athletic. Who got both goals for the Irons?

2. When West Ham drew 2-2 at Newcastle United on 10 January 2009 one of the home side's goals was scored by a player who would later join West Ham, while one of the away side's goals was scored by someone who had previously played for Newcastle. Who were the two men?

3. In the FA Cup West Ham reached the fifth round after wins against Barnsley and Hartlepool United, but lost to Middlesbrough after a replay. Who scored for the latter in both cup ties and eventually joined West Ham?

4. The only time the Hammers came to life in the League Cup was in extra time in their first match at Upton Park. They were held 1-1 after 90 minutes by a team three divisions below them, but came good in the extra half-hour to win 4-1. Who did they beat?

5. Unfortunately that was as far as they got, going down 1-0 at Watford in the next round through an own goal by which player?

6. Who was West Ham's top Premier League goalscorer with ten?

7. On 4 March 2009, West Ham won 1-0 away in the Premier League in front of the smallest crowd of the season in that division. 14,169 watched them win away to which club?

8. Who was the only player to appear in all 38 league games for the club?

9. Which central-defender missed just one?

10. He sounds like he stepped out of a Wagner opera, but which new signing got West Ham's winning goal against Stoke City at home and away during the season?

QUIZ No. 88

WEST HAM UNITED – SEASON 2009/10

1. West Ham finished the season one place above the long drop to the Championship and, although the players liked him, Gianfranco Zola was gone within two days of the season's end. When West Ham won 2-0 away on the opening day nobody thought that would be their only win on the road all season, but so it proved. Where did they win?

2. In the domestic cup competitions West Ham came up against two London clubs, going out of the FA Cup at the first hurdle at home to one of them, and beating the other 3-1 after extra time, also at home, in the League Cup before going out to Bolton Wanderers. Who were the two clubs?

3. Which young player scored a 93rd-minute winner for West Ham at Upton Park on 4 November 2009 against Aston Villa?

4. The most goals in a game involving West Ham came when Burnley visited Upton Park on 28 November 2009. What was the score?

5. West Ham found the net with penalties seven times in the Premier League. Cole, Jimenez and Noble got one each. Who scored the other four?

6. Who scored a great goal to beat Wigan Athletic 3-2 at Upton Park on 24 April 2010?

7. Three men who played in the Premier League for West Ham shared the first three letters of their surnames. Who were they?

8. Late goals came to West Ham's rescue against two London clubs at Upton Park in October. Both games ended 2-2 and Stanislav in the first one, and Diamanti in the second, got them a point in each case. Which two clubs were foiled?

9. Which ex-Hammer got Birmingham City's winning goal against the Londoners at St. Andrew's on 12 December 2009?

10. He played 33 times for West Ham in the Premier League, and scored one of their goals in the 3-0 home win over Hull City. If you drop one extra letter into his surname he becomes a French novelist as well as a footballer! Who is he?

QUIZ No. 89

WEST HAM UNITED - SEASON 2010/11

1. If, by some fluke, you just saw West Ham in the two domestic cup competitions then you watched them win eight of the ten games they played. If, on the other hand, you just saw them in the league, then your experience was somewhat different as they were relegated. Their first win of the season in the Premier League came in their sixth match when Piquionne's goal on 25 September 2010 beat which London rivals 1-0 at Upton Park?

2. West Ham met eight clubs in the domestic cup competitions, and one of those eight they encountered twice, beating them 3-1 after extra time in the League Cup, but going out of the FA Cup away to them in the quarter-final by 2-1. Who were they?

3. When the Irons drew 1-1 at Molineux on 16 October, the Wolves goal was scored by someone who would later play for West Ham. Who was he?

4. Which two clubs beginning with the same letter were relegated with West Ham?

5. Who scored a hat-trick when West Ham beat Nottingham Forest at Upton Park in the FA Cup fourth round by 3-2?

6. It was a great night at Upton Park when Manchester United were beaten 4-0 in the League Cup on 30 November 2010. Which two players shared the four goals equally?

7. Scott Parker made history when he won the FWA Footballer of the Year award with a relegated club and some critics were sniffy about it. I thought he deserved it even more because the team he played for were relegated! He was only two goals away from being their top league goalscorer as well. Who was he?

8.   After leading Manchester United 2-0 at Upton Park on 2 April 2011 it was disappointing to eventually lose the game 4-2. Which Manchester United scorer later joined West Ham?

9.   The misery of the League Cup semi-final away leg has been dealt with in an earlier section, but who were the only other club that West Ham played away to on their way to that semi-final when they won 2-1 before making their long way back to the capital?

10. The scorers of the two goals that gave Newcastle United three points at Upton Park on 23 October 2010 both found their way to the Hammers later in their careers. Who were they?

QUIZ No. 90

WEST HAM UNITED - SEASON 2011/12

1. West Ham made it back to the big time after just one season away when they were promoted through the play-offs under Sam Allardyce, with considerable assistance from his chief lieutenant Kevin Nolan. Along the way West Ham set a new club record for away wins with how many?

2. They lost just eight of their 46 games. Did they lose more at home, or away, or was it an even split?

3. Two West Ham players, who missed just one league game between them, were chosen in the Divisional Team of the Year at the season's end. Who were they?

4. Ricardo Vaz Te was a key addition in the January window when West Ham paid just £500,000 for his services and he repaid them with ten league goals and the vital play-off final winner. Which club sold him?

5. The domestic cup competitions were a disaster for West Ham. Which Yorkshire club ended their interest in the FA Cup in their first game in the competition?

6. The League Cup was even worse when they went down 2-1 at home to Aldershot from the fourth tier of English football. West Ham's goalscorer in that game therefore became their lone cup goalscorer. Who was he?

7. Which player who joined the club on a free transfer from Aston Villa at the start of the season grabbed an equaliser for the Hammers ten minutes from the end to make it 2-2 against Crystal Palace at Selhurst Park on 1 October 2011?

8. The aforementioned Ricardo Vaz Te got a hat-trick in West Ham's biggest win of the season at home to which club on 14 April 2012 when they delivered a 6-0 scoreline?

9. The season's biggest crowd in the Championship of 35,000 saw West Ham win their final game of the season 2-1 against Hull City but fail to gain automatic promotion. The scorer of their two goals in that game was their top league goalscorer with 14. Who was he?

10. West Ham returned to the promised land with a 2-1 play-off final victory following a 5-0 aggregate semi-final win. Which two clubs did they beat?

QUIZ No. 91

WEST HAM UNITED - SEASON 2012/13

1. West Ham achieved a respectable tenth place in the Premier League, and it was a particularly good season for one player who scored the winner away to his old club in November and topped the Premier League goalscorers at West Ham from midfield. Who was he?

2. West Ham were given a tough draw in the FA Cup third round when they were paired with Manchester United. They went out in a replay after holding their visitors 2-2 in the first match at Upton Park. Who scored both their goals in that game?

3. They lasted slightly longer in the League Cup where they beat Crewe Alexandra 2-0 before disappointingly going down 4-1 at home to Wigan. Only two West Ham players scored in that competition and both their surnames began with 'M'. Who were they?

4. One record that travelling fans would not be overjoyed about was that they scored the lowest number of away goals in the Premier League from their 19 matches played. How many?

5. Five other London clubs were in the Premier League with West Ham. They were Arsenal, Chelsea, Fulham, QPR and Spurs. Which was the only one that West Ham were undefeated against in the Premier League season?

6. On 9 December 2012 West Ham lost 3-2 at home to Liverpool. Two players, one from each side, put through their own net during the game. Who were they?

7. Who was the only man to be ever-present for all 38 Premier League games?

8. Which 'prodigal son' returned to the fold on a free transfer in January 2013, and, on the 19th of that month, found the net in a 1-1 Upton Park draw with QPR?

9. Which defender missed just two league games and was voted West Ham's Player of the Year?

10. The last day of the season brought a much-deserved hat-trick for Kevin Nolan in a 4-2 win at Upton Park against a club that were already relegated. Who were they?

QUIZ No. 92

WEST HAM UNITED - SEASON 2013/14

1. West Ham ended up 13th in the Premier League table but there were unsettling moments during the season when supporters were unhappy with the quality of football they were watching. The Hammers struggled again to score on their travels, finding the net 15 times, which was one goal less than which relegated London club?

2. It is ironic that Allardyce was made to field heavy criticism while the Crystal Palace manager, whose team also scored 15 away goals, was voted Manager of the Year. Who was he?

3. Who was the only West Ham player to appear in all 38 Premier League games?

4. West Ham led at half-time away at Norwich City on 9 November 2013 but let that slip in the second half, losing 3-1. The scorer of the second Norwich goal later became a Hammer. Who was he?

5. Later in the season West Ham suffered another 3-1 defeat, this time at Stoke City on 15 March 2014, when another goal against West Ham was credited to someone who later joined the club. Who was he?

6. Which two men shared the goalkeeping duties almost equally, one of them edging the other out by 20 to 18?

7. It was really hard for Irons fans to take what happened to the club in the two domestic cup competitions. Taking the FA Cup first, West Ham went out to a team from a lower division. That's happened a few times over the years, but not by the score they were beaten by Nottingham Forest at the first hurdle. What was that score?

8. The League Cup went very well until the disastrous semi-final when they went down by the incredible score of 9-0 on aggregate. Which Manchester City player scored five of the nine and was the only player to score in both legs?

9. On which London ground did West Ham win on twice during the season, by 3-0 and 2-1?

10. Who was the only West Ham player to score home and away in the club's run to the League Cup semi-final?

QUIZ No. 93

WEST HAM UNITED - SEASON 2014/15

1. West Ham reached the dizzy heights of fourth place in the Premier League before Christmas but won only three more times in the second half of the season to eventually end up in what position in the Premier League?

2. Given that they didn't qualify for the Europa League for the following season, how did they end up in it?

3. He was top league goalscorer for the club with ten goals, six of which came in successive games, and was also the only West Ham player to score in both domestic cup competitions. Who was he?

4. Which West Ham player was sent off at Upton Park on the first day of the season against Spurs?

5. West Ham's participation in the League Cup ended after a penalty shoot-out at Upton Park following a 1-1 draw after extra-time. The visitors' goal was an own goal by Winston Reid. Who were those visitors from Yorkshire?

6. Stewart Downing missed from the spot in the penalty shoot-out that decided the outcome of West Ham's replay against a northern club in the FA Cup. It didn't matter as nine other Hammers scored with their kicks after the 2-2 draw after extra-time at Upton Park. Who did they knock out?

7. They progressed past Bristol City with a 1-0 away win in the next round, before going out 4-0 to which Midlands club?

8. What did Adrian and Aaron Cresswell do in the 2014/15 season that no other West Ham player did?

9. When West Ham beat Swansea City 3-1 on 7 December 2014 the visitors' goalkeeper was shown a red card. Later in his career he joined West Ham. Who was he?

10. When West Ham won 2-1 at the Hawthorns against West Brom on 2 December 2014, the home side's goal was scored by someone who would eventually become a Hammer. Who was he?

QUIZ No. 94

WEST HAM UNITED – SEASON 2015/16

1. West Ham attained seventh place, their highest Premier League position thus far, after a strange start to the season when they lost their first two home games against Leicester City and Bournemouth, yet had wins of 2-0 and 3-0 away from home at two traditionally tough venues. Which two clubs did they beat?

2. West Ham seemed to have a need to pick up red cards. A goalkeeper, two defenders and two midfielders received one during the league season. They came at Upton Park against Leicester City, Bournemouth and Crystal Palace, and away at Liverpool and Watford. Which five Hammers received them?

3. Which player, who scored home and away against West Ham during this season, had now found the net against them in seven consecutive league and cup games?

4. Mauro Zarate scored for West Ham in an away League Cup tie, but it wasn't enough to save West Ham from a 2-1 defeat at the first hurdle in that competition when which Midlands club beat them after extra time?

5. West Ham had a good run in the FA Cup, beating, among others, Wolves and Liverpool before disappointingly losing at home to Manchester United after holding them at Old Trafford in the first tie. Which defender scored their goal at Upton Park when they went out 2-1 in the quarter-final?

6. Earlier, in the fourth-round replay against Liverpool at Upton Park, another defender had come up with the winner in extra time. Who was he?

7. Between the Liverpool and Manchester United ties, which club did West Ham beat 5-1 away from home in the fifth round?

8. Andy Carroll was top league goalscorer and had his greatest game for the Irons at Upton Park on 9 April 2016 when his hat-trick gave West Ham a 3-3 draw against which club?

9. In January, West Ham won 3-1 at Bournemouth and drew 2-2 at home to Manchester City. Who scored twice in each of those games?

10. The players on the pitch on the last night at Upton Park did the club proud when, after a thrilling contest Manchester United, were beaten 3-2. Everyone knows who scored the last goal on the ground, but which two West Ham players also scored that night?

QUIZ No. 95

WEST HAM UNITED - SEASON 2016/17

1. West Ham did finish top, but it was top of the bottom half of the Premier League. Their leading goalscorer in that league finished with nine goals, but in the early matches of the season he did manage to get five West Ham goals in a row. Who was he?

2. His nearest challenger on the goals front, whose tally put him just one behind, was also the player who spent more time on the pitch than any other Hammer. Who was he?

3. Finishing 11th wasn't so bad when you consider that West Ham made their worst start to a top-flight league season. How many of their first seven games did they win?

4. One club gave West Ham a terrible mauling, and not for the first time. In addition to winning the league games 3-1 and 4-0 they beat West Ham 5-0 at the London Stadium to end their interest in the FA Cup before it had begun. Who were they?

5. West Ham made heavy weather of their progress in the League Cup as well, needing a 96th-minute strike from Poyet to get past dogged Lancastrians from three divisions below them at the London Stadium in their first game in the competition. Which club refused to go quietly?

6. Which Premier League club did West Ham take care of by 2-1 at the London Stadium in the next round with goals from Kouyate and Fernandes?

7. Which Premier League club beat them 4-1 in the next round?

8. West Ham were on the wrong end of hat-tricks when they lost 5-1 at home to Arsenal and 3-2 at Bournemouth. Which two players inflicted the damage?

9. On 22 October, which West Ham defender sent the fans home happier than they might have been a moment earlier when he notched a 94th-minute winner at home to Sunderland?

10. In the return game at Sunderland on 15 April 2017 that finished 2-2, which West Ham player received a red card?

QUIZ No. 96

WEST HAM UNITED - SEASON 2017/18

1. After a season of considerable unrest, West Ham reached 13th place in the Premier League. Which new defender missed just one of the 38 league games?

2. Another new purchase started by getting sent off at Southampton, but by the season's end he was their top scorer with 11 league goals. Who was he?

3. There were murmurings when Brighton and Hove Albion won 3-0 at West Ham in October, but Slaven Bilic was sacked after a 4-1 home defeat on 4 November by which club?

4. West Ham sent Reece Burke out on loan at Bolton Wanderers at the start of the season, brought him back for a spell in January, and then loaned him out again for the rest of the season. In that short interlude he got an extra-time winner at the London Stadium in an FA Cup third-round replay against which club from two divisions below the Hammers?

5. Wigan Athletic checked West Ham's ambitions in that competition in the next round when which Hammers' winger saw a red card?

6. In the League Cup West Ham won 2-0 at Cheltenham, and then beat Bolton Wanderers 3-0 at home in the next round. Who scored in both games?

7. West Ham then came up against the two big fish in north London, knocking one of them out 3-2 on their own patch before going out of the competition 1-0 away to the other one. Which of the two did they beat?

8. It was a very difficult day at the London Stadium on 10 March 2018 when frustration about the running of the club boiled over. Which club's 3-0 defeat of West Ham on their own ground had been the spark for the heavy scenes that prevailed that day?

9. David Moyes did enough to gain West Ham a satisfactory place, and they celebrated with a 2-0 win at Leicester City, where who scored a superb 25-yard volley to make the game safe?

10. An interesting one to finish with. One brother scored for West Ham in the Premier League that season, while another scored against West Ham. Who were the two brothers?

QUIZ No. 97

WEST HAM UNITED – SEASON 2018/19

1. Manuel Pellegrini didn't make the best of starts as the new man at the head of things at West Ham. How many of their first ten Premier League games did they win?

2. Felipe Anderson put some smiles back on the faces of the West Ham fans with a hat-trick on 3 November 2018 when the Irons won 4-2 at home to which club?

3. Who was the only man to play in all 38 Premier League games?

4. Which London club did West Ham play away to twice in the domestic cup competitions, beating them 3-1 in the League Cup, but going out to them 4-2 in the FA Cup?

5. West Ham handed out a heavy beating in the next round of the League Cup when they won 8-0 at home to a club from the fourth tier of English football. Who were they?

6. When West Ham beat Manchester United 3-1 at the London Stadium on 29 September 2018, they badly needed to win the game. Which Manchester United defender helped them on their way with an own goal?

7. Which London club eventually knocked West Ham out of the League Cup 3-1 on West Ham's turf?

8. West Ham were losing 3-2 at home to soon to be relegated Huddersfield Town when which player turned the game on its head with goals in the 84th and 91st minutes to give the Hammers a 4-3 win on 16 March 2019?

9. Which West Ham player received a red card in a 1-1 draw at Leicester City on 27 October 2018 in the Premier League?

10. West Ham finished the season strongly with three straight wins, starting with a 1-0 success at Spurs, followed by a 3-0 win over Southampton at home, and ending with a 4-1 away win on the last day. The win was significant because it allowed West Ham to leapfrog over the team they had beaten and secure tenth place. Who were they?

QUIZ No. 98

WEST HAM UNITED - SEASON 2019/20

1. It was something of a shock to the system to lose the first game of the season 5-0 at home to Manchester City, especially as nearly 60,000 witnessed it, but on 24 August 2019 West Ham won the third game of the season 3-1 at Watford. Which new signing got off the mark with two of the three goals?

2. After winning just three of their first 13 games, West Ham must have been relieved when they won 1-0 away to Chelsea on 30 November 2019. Who came up with the winner?

3. Which West Ham player never missed a Premier League game all season?

4. Three days after Christmas manager Manuel Pellegrini was gone following a 2-1 home defeat to which Midlands club?

5. If you want a new broom to sweep things away and start anew I guess the first day of the new year is an appropriate time to put it all in place. David Moyes was brought back and on that first day of the year he started with a 4-0 home win over which club?

6. West Ham's leading league goalscorer had a total of ten goals, which was the same number as the player who won it the previous season had. Their surnames also started with the same letter. Who were the two men?

7. In the FA Cup West Ham beat Gillingham before going out to West Brom, while in the League Cup they beat Newport County before succumbing to Oxford United. Which player scored for them in both competitions?

8. The pandemic produced some crazy situations that are unlikely to be repeated. For example, West Ham's last game before the lockdown came on 7 March 2020 in front of 60,335 spectators, while their next game in the Premier League, on 20 June, like the eight after it, was watched by nobody! West Ham lost the first one away 1-0 and the second one at home 2-0. Which two clubs beat them?

9. On the first day of February which West Ham player scored two of their goals in a 3-3 home draw with Brighton?

10. Michail Antonio really went to town against Norwich City at Carrow Road, grabbing all four of West Ham's goals in their 4-0 win. You can have very long odds against another West Ham player scoring four goals in a league game in July, but that's what happened this time around. No West Ham player had scored four times in the league since 1981. Who did so in that year?

QUIZ No. 99

WEST HAM UNITED - SEASON 2020/21

1. Although they didn't get to see any of the action the season turned out to be a pleasant surprise for Hammers fans after the prophecies of doom and gloom when they won half their games and finished sixth in the Premier League, bringing with it the dubious merits of the Europa League. One man started 38 league games, while another was on the field at some point in all of them. Who were the two players?

2. The greatest moment of the season was surely the injury-time leveller at Spurs on 18 October 2020 that made it 3-3 after Spurs had led 3-0 after 16 minutes. Whose superb shot saved the game for West Ham?

3. Which defender came up with West Ham's 80th-minute winner at Elland Road against Leeds United on 11 December 2020?

4. Who scored winning goals for West Ham twice inside four days when on 16 January 2021 he got the only goal of a home game against Burnley, and then, on the same pitch on the 19th, came up with the winner when they beat West Brom 2-1?

5. Jesse Lingard, on loan from Manchester United, made an immediate impact on 3 February 2021 when he grabbed two goals in a 3-1 away win on whose ground?

6. It was an eventful season for Craig Dawson. He scored for West Ham in the Premier League against Crystal Palace, Liverpool and Leeds United, was sent off at Newcastle, and got own goals two weeks running against Manchester United and Arsenal. As if that wasn't enough for a defender, he also got West Ham's first FA Cup goal of the season when they won 1-0 away in the third round. Who did they knock out?

7. Which West Ham United player scored twice in two League Cup games for them, the second brace coming in a 5-1 home win against Hull City?

8. When West Ham lost 1-0 at home to Chelsea on 24 April 2021 one of their players received a red card in the 81st minute, the victim of the modern madness that dictates that against all known science when you get the ball in a tackle you must at the point of impact stop any further forward movement. Who was he?

9. Which fellow Londoners did West Ham knock out of the League Cup 3-0 in their first game in that season's competition?

10. Who was the only West Ham United player to score in both domestic cup competitions?

QUIZ No. 100

WILD CARD

1. Which Yorkshire club did West Ham beat 5-4 at Upton Park in the Premier League on 12 February 2000?

2. In his career did Jimmy Greaves score more goals for West Ham or against them?

3. Who, on 28 December 1999, scored West Ham's last goal of the millennium in a 1-1 home draw with Derby County?

4. How are Peter Bennett, Dave Bickles and Jimmy Bloomfield linked in West Ham United's history, besides being three more in a long line of Bs?

5. The 1939/40 season lasted just three matches before war brought it to an end. Two of West Ham's games were at Upton Park against Fulham and Leicester City. The other one, which they won 3-1, necessitated a round trip of nearly 450 miles. Who did they play?

6. West Ham drew 0-0 at home to Leicester City on 5 December 1964 and then went the rest of the season without drawing again. How many matches were involved?

7. Who, at the age of 17, became the Premier League's youngest player when he kept goal for West Ham against Manchester City at Maine Road on New Year's Day of 1996?

8. When West Ham were promoted from Division Two in the 1922/23 season, what was extremely rare about the 63 goals they scored?

9. Which two players with the same surname were leading league goalscorer for West Ham exactly 50 years apart?

10. Who has the shortest surname among the list of West Ham's leading league goalscorer in a season?

ANSWERS

QUIZ No.1 - ANYTHING GOES

1. Lampard, Bonds and Brooking
2. Darren Randolph
3. Tony Gale and Ian Pearce
4. Chelsea
5. In those five seasons the club that knocked West Ham out went on to win it
6. Ray Houghton
7. Carlos Tevez
8. He scored past three different goalkeepers
9. Ian Wright and Freddie Ljungberg
10. Moyes

QUIZ No.2 - BIRTHPLACES

1. Welwyn Garden City
2. Clapton
3. Perth
4. Barking
5. Reading
6. Ilford
7. Basildon
8. Lisbon
9. Woolwich
10. St. Petersburg

QUIZ No.3 - THE BOLEYN - PART 1

1. The Memorial Recreation Ground, Canning Town
2. Millwall
3. C – 10,000
4. Charlton Athletic
5. Spurs
6. The chicken run
7. The Centenary Stand
8. The Dr. Martens Stand
9. The Queen
10. Frank Lampard Jnr

QUIZ No.4 - THE BOLEYN - PART 2

1. Charlton Athletic
2. Italy and Ivory Coast
3. E139AZ
4. Tevez and Messi
5. Bury
6. Rotherham and Sunderland
7. Paul Konchesky
8. Manchester United and Swansea City
9. Winston Reid
10. Bournemouth

QUIZ No.5 - BUBBLE BLOWING (FANS)

1. Alfred Hitchcock
2. Pixie Lott
3. Warren Mitchell
4. Paul McGinley
5. Sally Gunnell
6. Sebastian Faulks
7. Nicky Hawkins
8. David Essex
9. Graham Gooch
10. Ray Winstone

QUIZ No.6 - CRYPTIC HAMMERS - PART 1

1. Tommy Dixon
2. Neil Orr
3. John Charles
4. Ted McDougall
5. Jimmy Neighbour
6. Ken Tucker
7. Pat Holland
8. Ernie Gregory
9. Clyde Best
10. Tony Gale

QUIZ No.7 - CRYPTIC HAMMERS - PART 2

1. Christian Dailly
2. George McCartney
3. Adrian
4. Alan Dickens
5. Phil Woosnam
6. Geoff Pike
7. Brian Dear
8. Sam Small
9. Roy Stroud
10. Billy Dare

QUIZ No.8 - CRYPTIC HAMMERS - PART 3

1. Dave Swindlehurst
2. John McDowell
3. Jermain Defoe
4. Stewart Downing
5. Alan Devonshire
6. Mervyn Day
7. Billy Jennings
8. Steve Whitton
9. Ken Brown
10. David Cross

QUIZ No.9 - CRYPTIC HAMMERS - PART 4
1. Bobby Ferguson
2. Andy Malcolm
3. John Dick
4. Julian Dicks
5. George Parris
6. John Bond
7. Billy Bonds
8. Malcolm Allison
9. Dave Sexton
10. Ian Bishop

QUIZ No.10 - CRYPTIC HAMMERS - PART 5
1. Declan Rice
2. Robert Green
3. Rio Ferdinand
4. Arthur Featherstone
5. Hayden Mullins
6. Jimmy Bigden
7. David James
8. Jack Collison
9. George Kay
10. George Butcher

QUIZ No.11 - FA CUP FINAL OPPONENTS
1. Sunderland
2. Howard Kendall
3. Dick Pym
4. Steven Gerrard
5. Liam Brady
6. Alan Kelly of Preston North End and Pepe Reina of Liverpool
7. Jamie Carragher
8. Jennings
9. Doug Holden
10. Conway and Slough

QUIZ No.12 - FOREIGN AFFAIRS - PART 1
1. Corinthians
2. Toulouse
3. Villareal
4. Midtjylland
5. Al Jazira
6. Lyon
7. Olympiacos
8. Slavia Prague
9. Anderlecht
10. Banik Ostrava

QUIZ No.13 - FOREIGN AFFAIRS - PART 2
1. Fiorentina
2. Lazio
3. Eintracht Frankfurt
4. Real Betis
5. Marseille
6. Lens
7. Borussia Dortmund
8. Juventus
9. Benfica
10. Valencia

QUIZ No.14 - GOALKEEPERS
1. Ted Hufton and Shaka Hislop
2. Trick question – 344 each
3. David James
4. Jim Standen
5. His brilliance on the last day of the previous season denied Manchester United the title and ensured Blackburn Rovers won it instead
6. Leyton Orient
7. Sheffield Wednesday
8. Roy Carroll
9. Tom McAlister
10. Brian Rhodes with 61

QUIZ No.15 - GREENER GRASS (BEFORE)
1. Pablo Zabaleta
2. Teddy Sheringham
3. John Radford
4. Andy Carroll, Craig Bellamy and Stewart Downing
5. Jimmy Greaves
6. Stuart Pearson
7. David Burrows
8. Jesse Lingard
9. Lukasz Fabianski and Jack Wilshere
10. Liam Brady

QUIZ No.16 - GREENER GRASS (AFTER)
1. Glen Johnson
2. Matthew Etherington
3. Joe Cole
4. Tony Cottee
5. Noel Cantwell
6. Carlos Tevez
7. Bobby Moore
8. Hayden Mullins
9. Paul Ince
10. Frank Lampard Jnr

QUIZ No.17 – GREEN STREET GREATS – No. 1 – BILLY BONDS

1. Less – 95
2. Sheffield Wednesday and Southampton
3. Spurs and QPR
4. True – 6-5
5. Manchester United
6. 9 and 11
7. They were the teams he scored against in the League Cup
8. Cambridge United
9. In the home game he scored his only West Ham hat-trick and the away game provided the only instance of Billy Bonds and Bobby Moore scoring in the same game. Chelsea was Bobby's middle name!
10. Finland

QUIZ No.18 – GREEN STREET GREATS – No. 2 – TREVOR BROOKING

1. Burnley
2. Leicester City
3. West Brom
4. Stuart Pearson
5. True
6. Hungary
7. Eintracht Frankfurt
8. Score in the League Cup
9. Spurs
10. Newcastle United

QUIZ No.19 – GREEN STREET GREATS – No. 3 – JOHNNY BYRNE

1. 30
2. He was the first player from a Fourth Division club to be selected
3. Sheffield Wednesday and Sunderland
4. Fulham
5. Spurs
6. Portugal
7. Plymouth Argyle and Workington
8. Leyton Orient and Swindon Town
9. Cardiff City
10. South Africa

QUIZ No.20 – GREEN STREET GREATS – No. 4 – GEOFF HURST

1. Liverpool
2. Stoke City and West Brom
3. Charlton Athletic and Leyton Orient
4. Swindon Town
5. France
6. Newcastle United and Sunderland
7. Fulham and Bolton Wanderers

8. Argentina and Romania
9. Score an FA Cup hat-trick
10. He scored his last West Ham goal in Manchester against City, and his last England goal in Athens against Greece

QUIZ No.21 – GREEN STREET GREATS – No. 5 – FRANK LAMPARD SNR

1. Manchester City
2. Halifax Town
3. Stamford Bridge
4. 1973/74
5. Den Haag
6. Yugoslavia and Australia
7. Southend United
8. Southampton
9. Everton
10. Preston North End

QUIZ No.22 – GREEN STREET GREATS – No. 6 – ALVIN MARTIN

1. Aston Villa
2. Leeds United
3. Brazil
4. Fewer – 598
5. Birmingham City
6. Derby County
7. Highbury
8. Luton Town
9. None
10. Leyton Orient

QUIZ No.23 – GREEN STREET GREATS – No. 7 – BOBBY MOORE

1. Manchester
2. Wolves
3. Peru and Scotland
4. Spurs
5. Goodison Park
6. Sissons and Sealey
7. West Brom
8. Billy Wright
9. Norwich City and Hereford United
10. Ewood Park

QUIZ No.24 – GREEN STREET GREATS – No. 8 – MARK NOBLE

1. Hull City and Wolves
2. Coventry City
3. Spurs
4. Bulgaria and the Republic of Ireland
5. Ray Stewart
6. Leicester City
7. Steve Potts
8. Brighton
9. Watford
10. Grady Diangana

QUIZ No.25 - GREEN STREET GREATS - NO. 9 - PHIL PARKES
1. Sedgley
2. Walsall
3. Portugal
4. Trevor Brooking and Martin Peters
5. More - £525,000
6. Oldham Athletic
7. Lou Macari
8. False – Mervyn Day – 1975
9. Ipswich Town
10. Bobby Ferguson, Tom McAlister, Ludek Miklosko and Perry Suckling

QUIZ No.26 - GREEN STREET GREATS - NO. 10 - VIC WATSON
1. 42
2. Cardiff City and Coventry City
3. Brighton and Southampton
4. Eight
5. Aston Villa
6. Corinthians
7. Leeds United
8. Spurs
9. Vic Keeble
10. Liverpool

QUIZ No.27 - HAMMERS HEARD FROM (QUOTES)
1. Harry Redknapp
2. Paulo Di Canio
3. John Hartson on his assault on Eyal Berkovic
4. Jock Stein on Bobby Moore
5. Billy Bonds
6. Paul Ince
7. Brian Clough on Trevor Brooking
8. Alan Pardew on James Collins
9. Julian Dicks
10. Geoff Hurst on Bobby Moore

QUIZ No.28 - HELPING HANDS
1. Richard Rufus
2. Harry Kane
3. Tony Hibbert
4. Martin Skrtel
5. Ashley Westwood
6. Tony Warner, Jussi Jaaskelainen and Craig Gordon
7. James Chester
8. Ronald Zubar
9. Nobby Solano
10. Chris Samba

QUIZ No.29 - IF THE CAP FITS - PART 1 - ENGLAND
1. Ken Brown, Paul Goddard and Dean Ashton
2. Cole and Lampard
3. False – Alvin Martin as well
4. Peters, Parker and Carrick
5. Rob Green
6. 'C'
7. Johnny Byrne and Ian Wright
8. Geoff Hurst with 49 has a lead of two
9. Trevor Sinclair
10. Ferdinand, Pearce, Peters

QUIZ No.30 - IF THE CAP FITS - PART 2 - SCOTLAND AND WALES
1. James Collins and Danny Gabbidon
2. John Dick
3. Seven
4. Christian Dailly
5. Wimbledon
6. Ray Stewart and Frank McAvennie
7. Phil Woosnam
8. Don Hutchison
9. Andy Melville
10. Leeds United and Norwich City

QUIZ No.31 - IF THE CAP FITS - PART 3 - NORTHERN IRELAND AND THE REPUBLIC OF IRELAND
1. Grant McCann
2. Darren Randolph
3. Iain Dowie
4. Gary Breen
5. Jimmy Quinn
6. More – 53
7. Michael Hughes
8. David Connolly
9. Allen McKnight and Roy Carroll
10. Liam Brady

QUIZ No.32 - IF THE CAP FITS - PART 4 - OVERSEAS PLAYERS
1. Switzerland
2. Trinidad and Tobago
3. Australia
4. Ukraine
5. Denmark
6. Sierra Leone
7. Peru
8. USA
9. Belgium
10. Costa Rica

QUIZ No.33 - LATER IN LIFE
1. Frank O'Farrell and Dave Sexton
2. Stuart Pearce
3. Mervyn Day
4. John Bond
5. Dave Sexton, Geoff Hurst and Frank Lampard Jnr
6. Harry Redknapp
7. Malcolm Allison
8. Paul Ince
9. Martin Peters
10. Glen Roeder and Chris Hughton

QUIZ No.34 - MANAGERS
1. Syd King and Charlie Paynter
2. Gianfranco Zola
3. Sam Allardyce
4. Alan Pardew and Alan Curbishley
5. Harry Redknapp
6. Ron Greenwood
7. Ronnie Boyce, Trevor Brooking and Kevin Keen
8. Lou Macari and Manuel Pellegrini
9. John Lyall
10. Avram Grant

QUIZ No.35 - MULTIPLE CHOICE
1. B – 30p
2. C – Spurs
3. A – Falkirk
4. D – QPR
5. C – Wimbledon
6. A – Alan Pardew
7. C – 13th
8. B – 24 million
9. D – Arsenal
10. A – Team Coach

QUIZ No.36 - POT LUCK
1. Brentford
2. Steve Death
3. Cannes
4. Scott Parker
5. 11
6. Moore, Young and Jennings
7. Bobby Gould
8. Chelsea
9. West Brom
10. Johnny Byrne

QUIZ No.37 - SEEING RED
1. Frederic Piquionne
2. James Tomkins
3. Paul Konchesky
4. Sofiane Feghouli
5. Carlton Cole
6. Michail Antonio
7. Morgan Amalfitano
8. Andy Carroll
9. Victor Obinna
10. Millwall, Southampton and Blackpool

QUIZ No.38 - TEN TOP HAMMERS - PART 1
1. Noel Cantwell
2. Tony Cottee
3. Jack Tresadern
4. Syd Puddefoot
5. Martin Peters
6. Jimmy Ruffell
7. Ray Stewart
8. Ernie Gregory
9. John Dick
10. Bryan 'Pop' Robson

QUIZ No.39 - TEN TOP HAMMERS - PART 2
1. Crystal Palace
2. Watford and Maidenhead United
3. 1940
4. Dagenham and Redbridge
5. Liverpool
6. Birmingham City
7. Sheffield United
8. Jack Charlton
9. Blackburn Rovers
10. Leyton Orient – and he was chief administrator and commissioner of the North American Soccer League

QUIZ No.40 - THAMES IRONWORKS AND WEST HAM UNITED - LEAGUE FOOTBALL 1896-1915
1. Brentford
2. Shepherds Bush
3. Maidenhead United
4. Fulham
5. Gravesend
6. Billy Grassam
7. Spurs, Fulham and QPR
8. Danny Shea
9. 7-4 to West Ham
10. Norwich City

QUIZ No.41 - TRANSFERS - 1945-60 - PART 1
1. Colchester United
2. Preston North End
3. Spurs
4. Brentford
5. Leyton Orient
6. Reading
7. Norwich City
8. Wolves
9. Newcastle United
10. Luton Town

QUIZ No.42 - TRANSFERS 1945-60 - PART 2

1. Leyton Orient
2. Colchester United
3. Brighton
4. Wolves
5. Spurs
6. Chelsea
7. Preston North End
8. Notts County
9. Reading
10. Brentford

QUIZ No.43 - TRANSFERS 1960-75 - PART 1

1. Crystal Palace
2. Chelsea
3. Luton Town
4. Sheffield Wednesday
5. Manchester United
6. Rochdale
7. Bristol City
8. Norwich City
9. Sunderland
10. Watford

QUIZ No.44 - TRANSFERS 1960-75 - PART 2

1. Brentford
2. Stoke City
3. Leyton Orient
4. Crystal Palace
5. Spurs
6. Charlton Athletic
7. Chelsea
8. Torquay United
9. Millwall
10. Sheffield Wednesday

QUIZ No.45 - TRANSFERS 1975-90 - PART 1

1. Norwich City
2. West Brom
3. QPR
4. Lincoln City
5. Oldham Athletic
6. Fulham
7. Manchester City
8. Bury
9. Coventry City
10. Derby County

QUIZ No.46 - TRANSFERS 1975-90 - PART 2

1. Fulham
2. Birmingham City
3. Blackburn Rovers
4. Charlton Athletic
5. Crystal Palace
6. Huddersfield Town
7. Cardiff City
8. Spurs
9. Chelsea
10. Leyton Orient

QUIZ No.47 - TRANSFERS 1990-2005 - PART 1

1. Glasgow Rangers
2. Portsmouth
3. Swindon Town
4. Spurs
5. Everton
6. Arsenal
7. Aston Villa
8. Crystal Palace
9. Manchester City
10. Derby County

QUIZ No.48 - TRANSFERS 1990-2005 - PART 2

1. Birmingham City
2. Leyton Orient
3. Celtic
4. Brentford
5. Bristol City
6. Portsmouth
7. Leicester City
8. Wimbledon
9. Charlton Athletic
10. Manchester City

QUIZ No.49 - TRANSFERS 2005-20 - PART 1

1. Barnsley
2. Norwich City
3. Manchester United
4. Birmingham City
5. Newcastle United
6. Cardiff City
7. Wolves
8. Fulham
9. Ipswich Town
10. Nottingham Forest

QUIZ No.50 - TRANSFERS 2005-20 - PART 2

1. Norwich City
2. Fulham
3. Newcastle United
4. Crystal Palace

5. Swansea City
6. Birmingham City
7. Liverpool
8. Aston Villa
9. Sunderland
10. Stoke City

QUIZ No.51 - TRUE OR FALSE
1. True
2. True
3. False – Everton won 3-2 in 1966
4. True
5. False – they did so in 1985/86
6. True
7. False – Des Walker of Nottingham Forest vs Spurs in 1991, and Tommy Hutchison of Manchester City vs Spurs in 1981
8. True
9. False – Clive Allen won it at Spurs
10. True

QUIZ No.52 - VENUES
1. Stamford Bridge
2. Elland Road
3. Gent
4. Park Avenue, Bradford
5. Molineux
6. The Heysel Stadium
7. Hillsborough
8. Anfield
9. Four
10. The Hawthorns, Upton Park, Wembley and Villa Park

QUIZ No.53 - WEST HAM UNITED IN THE EUROPEAN CUP WINNERS' CUP 1964/65 AND 1965/66
1. Ronnie Boyce
2. Johnny Byrne
3. Brian Dear
4. Sparta Prague
5. Alan Dickie
6. Olympiakos
7. FC Magdeburg and Borussia Dortmund
8. John Bond
9. Real Zaragoza
10. Geoff Hurst

QUIZ No.54 - WEST HAM UNITED IN THE EUROPEAN CUP WINNERS' CUP 1975/76 AND 1980/81
1. Den Haag
2. Billy Jennings
3. The away-goals rule
4. Trevor Brooking
5. Francois Van Der Elst

6. David Cross and Castilla
7. Zero – the authorities punished West Ham for previous fan unrest and the game was played behind closed doors. However, 262 is also an acceptable answer as it seems that was the actual number inside the ground.
8. Billy Bonds
9. Stuart Pearson
10. They stopped West Ham scoring

QUIZ No.55 - WEST HAM UNITED IN EUROPE - 1999-2017 - PART 1
1. The Intertoto Cup
2. Finland and Holland
3. Metz
4. Frank Lampard Jnr
5. Marc Vivien-Foe
6. Steaua Bucharest
7. Trevor Sinclair
8. Palermo
9. Roy Carroll
10. David Di Michele

QUIZ No.56 - WEST HAM UNITED IN EUROPE - 1999-2017 - PART 2
1. Andorra and Malta
2. Diafra Sakho
3. James Tomkins
4. Collins got the red card and Ogbonna put through his own net
5. Valencia
6. Mauro Zarate
7. Slovenia
8. Cheikhou Kouyate
9. Mark Noble
10. A – 3,360

QUIZ No.57 - WEST HAM UNITED IN FA CUP FINALS - PART 1 - CLUBS
1. Bolton Wanderers and Fulham
2. They shared the same colours
3. 1923
4. 2006
5. Three
6. Sheffield Wednesday
7. None
8. No
9. Liverpool
10. 2006

QUIZ No.58 - WEST HAM UNITED IN FA CUP FINALS - PART 2 - PLAYERS

1. John Sissons
2. Brown and Moore
3. B, S, H and M
4. Ronnie Boyce and Trevor Brooking
5. Paul Konchesky
6. Alan Taylor
7. Teddy Sheringham
8. Paul Allen
9. Taylor
10. Stuart Pearson

QUIZ No.59 - WEST HAM UNITED IN THE FA CUP - 1895-1915

1. Chatham
2. Newcastle United
3. Aston Villa
4. Stamford Bridge
5. George Webb
6. Liverpool
7. Gillingham
8. Blackburn
9. Billy Grassam
10. Dartford

QUIZ No.60 - WEST HAM UNITED IN THE FA CUP - 1919-39

1. Bury
2. Spurs
3. Eight
4. Chelsea
5. Hull City, Brighton, Southampton and Plymouth Argyle
6. Corinthians
7. Brentford
8. Vic Watson
9. Ashton Gate, Bristol
10. Loftus Road, Upton Park, White Hart Lane and Highbury. They won at QPR, drew at home with Spurs, drew away in the replay and played a third match with them at the neutral ground of Highbury which they won

QUIZ No.61 - WEST HAM UNITED IN THE FA CUP - 1945-60

1. Seven
2. Arsenal
3. Blackpool
4. Grimsby Town
5. Spurs
6. John Dick
7. No
8. Albert Foan
9. White Hart Lane
10. Bill Shankly and Denis Law

QUIZ No.62 - WEST HAM UNITED IN THE FA CUP - THE 1960S

1. Charlton Athletic and Leyton Orient
2. Peter Brabrook
3. Chelsea
4. Plymouth Argyle
5. Stoke City, Swindon Town and Sheffield United
6. 1962/63
7. Burnley
8. Mansfield Town and Middlesbrough
9. Geoff Hurst
10. Swindon Town

QUIZ No.63 - WEST HAM UNITED IN THE FA CUP - THE 1970S

1. Blackpool
2. Brian Dear, Clyde Best, Bobby Moore and Jimmy Greaves
3. Huddersfield Town, Hull City and Hereford United
4. Southampton and Swindon Town
5. Upton Park, Highbury, Stamford Bridge and Wembley
6. QPR
7. Newport County
8. Edgar Street, Hereford
9. Geoff Hurst
10. Alan Taylor scored all six of their goals in three lots of two

QUIZ No.64 - WEST HAM UNITED IN THE FA CUP - THE 1980S

1. Aston Villa
2. QPR
3. Charlton Athletic
4. Manchester United
5. Sheffield Wednesday
6. Wrexham and Watford
7. Leroy Rosenior
8. Paul Goddard and Tony Cottee
9. Torquay United
10. Sheffield and London

QUIZ No.65 - WEST HAM UNITED IN THE FA CUP - THE 1990S

1. Aldershot and Farnborough Town
2. Kidderminster and Emley
3. Blackburn Rovers
4. Bernard Lama
5. Swansea City and Wrexham
6. Martin Allen
7. They had endured three draining scraps with Liverpool to earn the right to play West Ham
8. Trevor Morley
9. Luton Town
10. Grimsby Town, Wrexham, Luton Town and Tranmere Rovers

QUIZ No.66 - WEST HAM UNITED IN THE LEAGUE - 1919-39

1. Barnsley and Everton
2. Joe Cockcroft
3. Syd Puddefoot and Port Vale
4. Coventry City
5. Notts County and Leicester City
6. Arsenal
7. Manchester United
8. Billy Ruffell
9. Chesterfield
10. Bolton Wanderers

QUIZ No.67 - WEST HAM UNITED IN THE LEAGUE - 1946-60

1. Fred Neary
2. Ken Tucker
3. QPR
4. Eric Parsons and Andy Malcolm
5. Tommy Dixon, Billy Dare and John Dick
6. Sheffield United
7. Alan Blackburn
8. 7-2 to West Ham
9. Vic Keeble
10. Sheffield Wednesday

QUIZ No.68 - WEST HAM UNITED IN THE LEAGUE - THE 1960S

1. 5-5
2. John Dick and Malcolm Musgrove
3. Fulham
4. Arsenal
5. Manchester City
6. Birmingham City
7. Liverpool and London
8. 18
9. Leicester City
10. Manchester City – yet again!

QUIZ No.69 - WEST HAM UNITED IN THE LEAGUE - THE 1970S

1. David Cross
2. Trevor Brooking
3. Tommy Taylor
4. Sunderland
5. Billy Jennings
6. Burnley and Birmingham City
7. Notts County, Newcastle United and Cambridge United
8. Shrewsbury Town
9. Derek Hales
10. Burnley

QUIZ No.70 - WEST HAM UNITED IN THE LEAGUE - THE 1980S

1. QPR
2. Grimsby Town and Spurs
3. Paul Goddard
4. Dave Swindlehurst
5. Everton
6. Highfield Road and Loftus Road
7. Millwall
8. Leeds United
9. Leroy Rosenior and Jimmy Quinn
10. Phil Parkes, Tony Gale, Mark Ward and Tony Cottee

QUIZ No.71 - WEST HAM UNITED IN THE LEAGUE - THE 1990S

1. Oldham Athletic and Hull City
2. Frank McAvennie
3. Cambridge United, Portsmouth and Newcastle United
4. Martin Allen
5. Michael Hughes
6. John Hartson
7. Barnsley
8. Derby County and Leeds United
9. Manchester United
10. Trevor Morley

QUIZ No.72 - WEST HAM UNITED IN LEAGUE CUP FINALS AND SEMI-FINALS - PART 1 - CLUBS

1. True
2. Cardiff City and Coventry City
3. Luton Town and Manchester City
4. West Brom
5. Oldham Athletic and Manchester City
6. Stoke City
7. Leicester City
8. Birmingham City
9. Cardiff City
10. Liverpool

QUIZ No. 73 - WEST HAM UNITED IN LEAGUE CUP FINALS AND SEMI-FINALS - PART 2 - PLAYERS

1. Johnny Byrne, Bobby Moore and Martin Peters
2. Ray Stewart
3. Paul Goddard
4. Geoff Hurst
5. Julian Dicks
6. Carlton Cole
7. Lee Bowyer
8. West Brom
9. Gordon Banks and Bobby Ferguson
10. Bobby Moore

QUIZ No.74 - WEST HAM UNITED IN THE LEAGUE CUP - THE 1960S
1. Charlton Athletic
2. Aston Villa and Rotherham
3. 6-0
4. Johnny Byrne
5. Bristol Rovers and Grimsby Town
6. Leeds United
7. Johnny Sissons and Geoff Hurst
8. Malcolm Musgrove
9. Bolton Wanderers
10. Plymouth Argyle

QUIZ No.75 - WEST HAM UNITED IN THE LEAGUE CUP - THE 1970S
1. Hull City and Coventry City
2. Fulham, QPR and Spurs
3. Nottingham Forest
4. They drew both home games and won the replays away
5. Bryan Robson
6. Bristol City
7. Tranmere Rovers
8. Bobby Gould and Bill Lansdowne
9. John McDowell
10. Stockport County and Swindon Town

QUIZ No.76 - WEST HAM UNITED IN THE LEAGUE CUP - THE 1980S
11. Liverpool
12. Derby County
13. David Cross
14. Paul Ince
15. Spurs
16. Manchester
17. Bury
18. Preston North End
19. Notts County
20. Birmingham

QUIZ No.77 - WEST HAM UNITED IN THE LEAGUE CUP - THE 1990S
1. Arsenal
2. Slaven Bilic
3. Southampton and Northampton
4. John Hartson and Frank Lampard Jnr
5. Don Hutchison
6. Chesterfield
7. Mike Small
8. Nottingham Forest
9. Aston Villa
10. Hugo Porfirio

QUIZ No.78 - WEST HAM UNITED IN OTHER COMPETITIONS
1. Blackburn Rovers
2. Liverpool
3. Coventry City
4. Derby County
5. Orient
6. Bristol Rovers

7. Leroy Rosenior
8. Fiorentina
9. C - 800
10. George Foreman

QUIZ No.79 - WEST HAM UNITED - SEASON 2000/01
1. Frederic Kanoute
2. Manchester United
3. Walsall
4. Sheffield Wednesday
5. Don Hutchison
6. Christian Dailly
7. Ian and Stuart Pearce
8. David Unsworth
9. Igor Stimac
10. Svetoslav Todorov

QUIZ No.80 - WEST HAM UNITED - SEASON 2001/02
1. Sebastien Schemmel
2. Everton and Blackburn Rovers
3. Jermain Defoe
4. Macclesfield
5. Reading
6. Charlton Athletic
7. Paul Kitson
8. Les Ferdinand
9. Old Trafford
10. Ian Pearce

QUIZ No.81 - WEST HAM UNITED - SEASON 2002/03
1. Paulo Di Canio
2. Trevor Sinclair and Jermain Defoe
3. Oldham Athletic
4. Marlon Harewood
5. Because Fortune 'came out of hiding' to score one of Charlton's goals
6. Teddy Sheringham and Frederic Kanoute
7. Jermain Defoe
8. Nobby Solano
9. Craig Bellamy
10. Birmingham City

QUIZ No.82 - WEST HAM UNITED - SEASON 2003/04
1. Ipswich Town
2. Crystal Palace
3. Tomas Repka
4. Matthew Etherington
5. Fulham and Spurs
6. Sheffield United
7. Cardiff City
8. Paul Kitson
9. Brian Deane
10. Marlon Harewood

QUIZ No.83 - WEST HAM UNITED - SEASON 2004/05
1. Sunderland
2. Watford
3. Anton Ferdinand

4. Preston North End
5. True
6. Sheffield United and Chelsea
7. Teddy Sheringham
8. 5-0
9. Cardiff City, Wolves, Leicester City and Reading
10. Dean Ashton

QUIZ No.84 - WEST HAM UNITED - SEASON 2005/06

1. Bolton Wanderers
2. Marlon Harewood
3. Bobby Zamora
4. Aston Villa
5. Dean Ashton
6. Kevin Nolan
7. Lucas Neill
8. Hayden Mullins
9. Svetoslav Todorov
10. Lasagnegate and Jermain Defoe

QUIZ No.85 - WEST HAM UNITED - SEASON 2006/07

1. Nigel Reo-Coker
2. Brighton
3. Watford
4. Arsenal
5. Bobby Zamora
6. 6-0
7. Marlon Harewood
8. Nigel Reo-Coker
9. Carlos Tevez
10. 2-0 to West Ham

QUIZ No.86 - WEST HAM UNITED - SEASON 2007/08

1. 4-0
2. George McCartney
3. Craig Bellamy
4. Derby County
5. Manchester City and Everton
6. Scott Parker
7. Dean Ashton
8. Ashley Cole, Joe Cole and Carlton Cole
9. Anton Ferdinand and Matthew Upson
10. Carlos Tevez and Michael Carrick

QUIZ No.87 - WEST HAM UNITED - SEASON 2008/09

1. Dean Ashton
2. Andy Carroll and Craig Bellamy
3. Stewart Downing
4. Macclesfield Town
5. Hayden Mullins
6. Carlton Cole

7. Wigan Athletic
8. Rob Green
9. Matthew Upson
10. Diego Tristan

QUIZ No.88 - WEST HAM UNITED - SEASON 2009/10

1. Wolves
2. Arsenal and Millwall
3. Zavron Hines
4. 5-3 to West Ham
5. Alessandro Diamanti
6. Scott Parker
7. Carlton Cole, James Collins and Jack Collison
8. Fulham and Arsenal
9. Lee Bowyer
10. Julien Faubert

QUIZ No.89 - WEST HAM UNITED - SEASON 2010/11

1. Spurs
2. Stoke City
3. Matt Jarvis
4. Blackpool and Birmingham City
5. Victor Obinna
6. Jonathan Spector and Carlton Cole
7. Demba Ba
8. Javier Hernandez
9. Sunderland
10. Kevin Nolan and Andy Carroll

QUIZ No.90 - WEST HAM UNITED - SEASON 2011/12

1. 13
2. An even split
3. Mark Noble and James Tomkins
4. Barnsley
5. Sheffield Wednesday
6. Junior Stanislas
7. John Carew
8. Brighton
9. Carlton Cole
10. Cardiff City and Blackpool

QUIZ No.91 - WEST HAM UNITED - SEASON 2012/13

1. Kevin Nolan
2. James Collins
3. Modibo Maiga and Nicky Maynard
4. 11
5. QPR
6. Steven Gerrard and James Collins
7. Jussi Jaaskelainen
8. Joe Cole
9. Winston Reid
10. Reading

QUIZ No.92 - WEST HAM UNITED - SEASON 2013/14
1. Fulham
2. Tony Pulis
3. Mark Noble
4. Robert Snodgrass
5. Marco Arnautovic
6. Adrian (20) and Jaaskelainen (18)
7. 5-0
8. Alvaro Negredo
9. White Hart Lane
10. Matt Jarvis

QUIZ No.93 - WEST HAM UNITED - SEASON 2014/15
1. 12th
2. By topping the Fair Play League
3. Diafra Sakho
4. James Collins
5. Sheffield United
6. Everton
7. West Brom
8. Played all 38 league games
9. Lukasz Fabianski
10. Craig Dawson

QUIZ No.94 - WEST HAM UNITED - SEASON 2015/16
1. Arsenal and Liverpool
2. Adrian, Jenkinson, Noble, Collins and Kouyate
3. Romelu Lukaku
4. Leicester City
5. James Tomkins
6. Angelo Ogbonna
7. Blackburn Rovers
8. Arsenal
9. Enner Valencia
10. Diafra Sakho and Michail Antonio

QUIZ No.95 - WEST HAM UNITED - SEASON 2016/17
1. Michail Antonio
2. Manuel Lanzini
3. One
4. Manchester City
5. Accrington Stanley
6. Chelsea
7. Manchester United
8. Alexis Sanchez and Josh King
9. Winston Reid
10. Sam Byram

QUIZ No.96 - WEST HAM UNITED - SEASON 2017/18
1. Pablo Zabaleta
2. Marco Arnautovic
3. Liverpool
4. Shrewsbury Town
5. Arthur Masuaka
6. Diafra Sakho
7. Spurs
8. Burnley
9. Mark Noble
10. Ayew – Andre and Jordan

QUIZ No.97 - WEST HAM UNITED - SEASON 2018/19
1. Two
2. Burnley
3. Lukasz Fabianski
4. Wimbledon
5. Macclesfield Town
6. Victor Lindelof
7. Spurs
8. Javier Hernandez
9. Mark Noble
10. Watford

QUIZ No.98 - WEST HAM UNITED - SEASON 2019/20
1. Sebastien Haller
2. Aaron Cresswell
3. Declan Rice
4. Leicester City
5. Bournemouth
6. Marco Arnautovic and Michail Antonio
7. Pablo Fornals
8. Arsenal and Wolves
9. Robert Snodgrass
10. David Cross

QUIZ No.99 - WEST HAM UNITED - SEASON 2020/21
1. Tomas Soucek and Jarrod Bowen
2. Manuel Lanzini
3. Angelo Ogbonna
4. Michail Antonio
5. Aston Villa
6. Stockport County
7. Sebastien Haller
8. Fabian Balbuena
9. Charlton Athletic
10. Andriy Yarmolenko

QUIZ No.100 - WILD CARD
1. Bradford City
2. Against – 16 to 13
3. Paulo Di Canio
4. They were the only three substitutes West Ham used in the 1965/66 season when they were allowed for the first time
5. Plymouth Argyle
6. 22
7. Neil Finn
8. They scored twice as many away as they did at home
9. Wright – Ken in 1948/49 and Ian in 1998/99
10. Demba Ba